best *wine* buys
in the high street

2002

best wine buys

in the high street

2002

ned halley

foulsham
LONDON • NEW YORK • TORONTO • SYDNEY

foulsham

The Publishing House
Bennetts Close, Cippenham, Berkshire SL1 5AP, England

ISBN 0-572-02747-8

Text copyright © 2002 Ned Halley

Series, format and layout design © 2002 W. Foulsham & Co. Ltd

Printed in Great Britain by Cox & Wyman Ltd, Reading, Berkshire.

CONTENTS

A personal note

It's been a good year. The choice of wines available in Britain has continued to widen and prices, helped by sterling's strength against southern-hemisphere currencies as well as those of our continental neighbours, have not risen noticeably. The Budget that preceded the General Election left UK excise duty where it was – a mere £1.16 per bottle – and according to Customs & Excise, the financial year 2000–2001 was the first in history in which British consumers spent more on wine than they did on beer.

But in another sense it's been an uncomfortable year, because for all the growth in the wine market I have discovered that the choice offered by the dominant retailers – the supermarkets and few remaining high-street merchant chains – has become progressively, in fact quite rapidly, dominated by big brand names.

Multinational companies have moved into wine production, and producers who were once very modest in scale have grown and amalgamated into giants. Australia, now about to displace France as the biggest national supplier of wines to Britain, is a case in point. Jacob's Creek wines, the range that introduced so many of us to the delights of modern, fresh, 'upfront' Aussie reds and whites, is now by a mile the biggest brand in Britain. The producing company, Orlando, has grown exponentially as sales expanded, but is now owned by the French drinks giant Pernod-Ricard – a company with huge influence in the retail drinks trade worldwide, and able to offer terms to British supermarkets that no small-scale winegrower can hope to match.

Likewise another very big Australian enterprise, Southcorp, which owns famous brands such as Penfolds and Lindemans, has in 2001 blended itself with the only slightly smaller producer Rosemount to form what the new giant styles 'the world's largest premium-quality wine company'. Just after announcing this merger, Southcorp upped the price of several of its wines in the UK by a cool 25 per cent. This may have been to help raise the Aus$1.4 billion it needed to pay for Rosemount, but either way it left me in no doubt that when wine producers get this big they seem to think they can do what they like. Brands like Lindemans 65 Chardonnay and 45 Shiraz – both wildly praised by me in last year's edition of *Best Wine Buys* – were hoiked up from £4.99 to £5.99 and none of the retailers (bar the Co-op which has delisted them) seemed to bat an eye.

What I'm suggesting is that if these huge companies are to be allowed to monopolise the market, no matter how good their wines are, it's we consumers who will pay the price. Retailers such as Sainsbury's and Tesco like dealing with outfits on the scale of Pernod-Ricard and Southcorp, because they're computerised and efficient, they back their products with vast advertising budgets and no doubt do a nice line in corporate hospitality – it's not just morally equivocal wine journalists who get free trips to the Barossa, but wine-trade and grocery executives too.

The point I'm trying to make is that big brands, never mind big business as a whole, doesn't necessarily serve the interests of shoppers. Wine lovers who are interested enough to buy a book like this will, I hope, heed the brand threat and make determined efforts – assisted by the content of the following pages – to seek out individual wines in preference to those brands.

Consequently, this new edition of *Best Wine Buys* has far fewer big brand names in it than the previous ones have, and I have highlighted as many individual wines as I have found among the 3,000-or-so I have noted around the tastings I have attended and from among the samples I have tried at home during 2000–2001.

A big change in this year's *Best Wine Buys* is that the ceiling on price has been lifted to £10. This has certainly allowed me to include many more interesting, single-vineyard wines, but not, I hope, to the exclusion of bargain bottles under the all-important £5 mark – of which many hundreds still feature.

The scoring system

As an entirely subjective, not to say quirky, guide to relative value among the wines, I use a scoring scale of 0 to 12. During the past year, I have used this scale in all my notes and can rather gleefully admit that I have awarded a score of zero to 20-or-so wines. None of them, you might be relieved to know, appears in this book. And I have scored a very few wines costing under a tenner 11 or even 11/12 – but none (at any price) has achieved a full 12. I guess I dare not award a 12 in case the next I taste is something even better and I go off the sheet.

Most of the wines featured in this edition scored 8 or 9, which means they come recommended and I believe they are good value. If a wine scores 9/10 it's remarkably good value, and a straight 10 means I believe it is exceptionally delicious for the price. Anything marked 10/11 or above is quite simply a must-buy for anyone who enjoys the style of wine described.

As to the lower scores, those few wines marked 7 or less are not recommended as value for money, but are included for interest – either because they are decent wines that are overpriced or perhaps wines you might be tempted to buy because of their big brand name or gimmicky packaging, but which I found so disappointing I thought they merited a not-recommended warning.

But on the whole, wines I have not liked, I have simply left out. I must admit that these omissions include some of the best-known brands – especially from the United States, from where I have continued to find certain famous names of very disappointing quality indeed. I have not liked the relaunched and much-hyped Piat d'Or wines nor even the bluebottle version of Blue Nun, and these are among the many well-known brands you won't find here.

Also excluded are sparkling wines. Champagne at under £10 is extinct on this side of the Channel (but plentiful, you'll find, on the other side) and I remain mystified at the homogeneity of the sparkling wines of Spain (cava), which appear completely to have displaced the sparklers of Alsace and the Loire Valley which were once so refreshingly enjoyable. Antipodean and American sparkling wines are almost entirely dominated by the big brands (many owned, interestingly, by the big Champagne companies) and to me seem as alike each other as all those cavas.

Wine boxes are omitted, too. I don't feel they represent any improvement in value for money over bottled wines – and the saving, litre for litre, is rarely more than marginal between box and glass.

But the greatest number of exclusions in this book are, as before, those I have left out simply because I can't imagine anyone wanting to drink them. They are the wines that fail the 'so-what?' test. You know, as in answering the question: 'So what do you like about this wine?' If I have not been able to write down what that is, I cannot recommend the wine. I have to like a wine for a reason, and to be able to articulate that reason. Otherwise, I would be in no position to write a book such as this.

I do hope you will enjoy reading and using *Best Wine Buys*. I must, of course, apologise in advance for the inevitable fact that some of the wines mentioned will have been discontinued or replaced with a new vintage or increased in price by the time you are reading this. And I had better show contrition, too, for any disagreements readers may have with me over the comments I have made about individual wines.

Taste is personal in all things, and more so than most when it comes to wine. But I hope the impressions I have given of the hundreds of wines recommended in this guide will tempt you to try some new styles and flavours, and to look beyond all those beckoning brand names to the genuine, individual wines still clinging to their shelf space.

If *Best Wine Buys* arouses your curiosity about the wider world of wine, and encourages you to experiment, then it will have achieved its objective.

The choice

This book categorises the wines by nation of origin. This is largely because retailers sort their wines this way, but also because it is the country or region of origin that still most distinguishes one style of wine from another. True, wines are now commonly labelled most prominently with their constituent grape variety, but to classify all the world's wines into the small number of principal grape varieties would make for categories of an unwieldy size.

Chardonnay and Sauvignon Blanc are overwhelmingly dominant among whites, and four grapes, Cabernet Sauvignon, Merlot, Shiraz and Tempranillo, account for a very high proportion of red wines made worldwide.

But each area of production still – in spite of creeping globalisation – puts its own mark on its wines. Chardonnays from France remain (for the moment at least) quite distinct from those of Australia. Cabernet Sauvignon grown in a cool climate such as that of Bordeaux is a very different wine from Cabernet cultivated in the cauldron of the Barossa.

Of course there are 'styles' that winemakers worldwide seek to follow. Yellow, oaky Chardonnays of the type pioneered in South Australia are now made in South Africa, too – and in new, hi-tech wineries in New Zealand and Chile, Spain and Italy. But the variety is still wide. Even though the 'upfront' high-alcohol wines of the New World have grabbed so much of the market, France continues to make the elegant wines it has always made in its classic regions; Germany still produces racy, delicate Rieslings; and the distinctive zones of Italy, Portugal and Spain make ever-more characterful wines from indigenous grapes (as opposed to imported global varieties).

Among less-expensive wines, the theme is, admittedly, very much a varietal one. The main selling point for most wines costing under £10 is the grape of origin rather than the country of origin. It makes sense, because the characteristics of various grape varieties do a great deal to identify taste. A bottle of white wine labelled Chardonnay can reasonably be counted on to deliver that distinctive peachy or pineappley smell and soft, unctuous apple flavours. A Sauvignon Blanc should evoke gooseberries, green fruit and crisp freshness. And so on.

As to the best sources of wines under a tenner, it will take only a brief look through this book to reveal that some parts of the world appear to offer a far bigger choice of cheaper wines than others do. The classic regions of France –

Alsace, Bordeaux, Burgundy – make relatively few appearances, simply because their 'fine wines' are almost entirely priced above £10.

The wines of the Rhône and the Midi, including the vins de pays ('country wines'), on the other hand, appear very regularly. So do the wines of southern Italy, the emerging reactivated regions of Portugal and Spain and fast-expanding Argentina. All are proving a growing source of excellent-value wines.

And for all the domination of Chardonnay and Cabernet, there are plenty more grape varieties making their presence felt. Argentina, for example, has revived the fortunes of several French and Italian varieties that had become near-extinct at home. And the grape which (in my view) can make the most exciting of white wines, the Riesling, is now doing great things in the southern hemisphere as well as at home in Germany.

The global varieties are, indeed, everywhere, but this book describes wines made from no fewer than 60 different grape varieties (see A Brief Vocabulary starting on page 119) grown in every corner of the winemaking world. Let's hope this generous and growing choice is the shape of things to come.

Dark purple and reminiscent of port but delicious and not overstrong – £5.49 from Waitrose.

The state of the market

In Britain we drink about a billion bottles of wine each year. It sounds a lot, but comes only to about half a bottle of wine per head per week. Still, it's a start. Back in 1900, per capita wine consumption here was less than two bottles per year. This dismal level continued until the second half of the century, showing improvement only when foreign holidays became the norm, and large numbers of us suddenly discovered a taste for continental vices.

But long before the package-holiday era, Britain was nevertheless an important international market for wine. For centuries, keen imbibers here have been drinking more champagne, claret, moselle and port than in any other country. So when cheaper wines started to flood in during the 1960s, our wine trade was already geared up to take advantage of the new boom in low-margin plonk.

Unfortunately for the long-established specialist merchants, the supermarkets have scooped most of the market, but Britain has continued to be, as it has always been, the best country in the world in which to buy wine. Not the cheapest, thanks to a long Puritan tradition of trying to repress alcohol consumption through usurious excise duties, but with by far the widest range of sources.

In spite of the high costs prevailing here, Britain drinks more good-quality imported wine than any other country in the world. We are the most valued export market for several of the leading wine-producing nations.

Thus the astounding choice in the shops. Supermarkets carry from 500 to 700 distinct brands. The wine department in Safeway or Tesco can be depended upon to take up more space than bread, or meat. But shopping for wine is a rather more taxing task than choosing a loaf or picking out something for the Sunday roast.

Supermarkets on top

In a nation with so many traditional wine merchants, from grand London purveyors with Royal Warrants to tiny specialist firms importing the wines of just one region of France, it comes as a shock to find that three-quarters of all the wine bought 'off-licence' (for drinking at home) in Britain comes from supermarkets.

But are supermarkets selling quantity at the expense of quality? Not a bit of it. These huge companies take quality very seriously – among the bargain wines (nine out of every ten bottles sold in supermarkets cost under £5) as well as the 'fine' wines.

Tasting hundreds of supermarket wines every year as I do, I can honestly report finding few I could fairly describe as badly made or unpleasant to drink. But even making allowances for the jading effects of tasting scores of wines at one session, I must confess to one slightly troubling discovery. It is the striking homogeneity of an awful lot of wines. Far too many taste the same as each other.

Fair's fair, there is in some cases a simple explanation for this – because many supermarket 'own-brand' wines *are* the same as each other. Big producers in every part of the world happily apportion their harvests between two, three or more British supermarket chains, bottling the new wine in one giant operation with pauses merely for changing the labels.

And why not? The more outlets there are for the excellent wines of Argentina or Australia, the better. But the sameness problem isn't really about the enviable success of New World exporters. It's more about the uniformity of style. Supermarkets have convinced themselves that they know what their customers want. Most of the wines on the shelves conform not just to the prices dictated by the wine buyers, but to the styles they expect. Safeway, Sainsbury's and Tesco all have a hand in making many of the wines they sell, demanding that the products of wineries in every part of the world stick to the styles customers are perceived to demand.

This can hardly be faulted. But wine shoppers who do experiment with different wines on a regular basis will find that there can be a depressing similarity in, say, Chardonnay from sources as diverse as Hungary, Chile, South Africa and the far south of France. The wine-taster's party trick of identifying the nationality of an everyday wine is getting to be a very difficult one to perform with any hope of success.

That said, there is little room for complaint about the supermarkets. There is a terrific choice, and certainly plenty of commendable wines under a tenner. Thus, the very extensive sections devoted to some of the supermarkets in this book.

High-street combinations

When Britain's two biggest high-street off-licence chains, Thresher and Victoria Wine, announced their 1999 amalgamation under the strikingly odd name 'First Quench' they proclaimed that their combined network of shops would give them a 15 per cent share of the take-home wine market. It sounds impressive enough until you consider that Tesco alone, through its 566 supermarkets, was already selling more wine than all 3,000 First Quench shops put together.

Just two years later, First Quench has announced that it is to kill off the Victoria Wine name, except in Scotland, thus concluding the history of Britain's first, and once largest, high-street wine merchant. The merged chain is set to shrink to something like 2,000 outlets as Victoria Wine shops are closed down because they're too close to an existing Thresher to be 'rebranded' under the Thresher name – which will gradually be adopted for all the shops.

It's a sign of the times, because off-licences simply aren't cool any more. Wine in particular has become just another grocery item, and specialist retailers in this sector look destined to go the same way as their counterparts in bakery, butchery and fishmongery – by becoming just another aisle or counter in a gigantic hypermarket.

But it's only fair to point out that off-licences are in many ways much more attractive places in which to shop for wine than supermarkets. Prices are quite definitely competitive (it is a myth that supermarket wines are cheap) and if you're prepared to buy a dozen bottles of wine at a time most merchants will always give you 10 per cent off – double what can be expected in any supermarket.

Off-licences are forever running special promotions on their wines, too. In the struggle to compete with supermarkets, they have 'loyalty' schemes which outdo store 'points' cards by a mile for value. If you are even an occasional customer at a local branch of a major off-licence chain, don't hesitate to ask about any club-style arrangements they might have.

Fine-wine merchants

If the nationwide high-street off-licence chains have been squeezed by the hypermarkets, how much more so for the independently owned specialist wine merchants? It's a testimony to the enterprise of centuries-old firms such as Berry Bros & Rudd in London that they can continue to prosper in the age of the retail multiple – but they do.

In this edition, I have included alongside the supermarket giants a couple of very small specialist merchants who sell wines you simply will not find in the multiples, because they are growers' wines – chosen by the merchant by the infallible method of travelling to the producer's vineyard, tasting the wine and striking a deal on price.

The two merchants, Roger Harris and Tom Innes of Irma Fingal-Rock, are both specialists – in Beaujolais and Burgundy respectively. They know their regions and they know their wines and they are models of the kind of merchant all true wine enthusiasts should use. Both offer nationwide delivery based on a published list of wines and both charge prices that are in no way undercut by high-street or supermarket rivals – which don't, admittedly, sell these kind of highly individual wines anyway.

I've included these two small enterprises because they represent such a stark contrast with their huge rivals. There are many more such specialist importers in Britain and I hope to extend coverage of these in future *Best Wine Buys* editions.

This mature Ockfener Bockstein, at just £4.49, is among an extraordinary range of German bargains at Majestic.

The price of wine

How do retailers price their wines? Some bottles seem inexplicably cheap, others unjustifiably expensive. But there is often a simple explanation. Big retailers work to price points. In wine, these are £2.99, £3.49, £3.99, even £9.99. You'll find very few bottles priced anywhere between these 50p spacings. A wine that wouldn't be profitable at £4.99 but would be at, say, £5.11, is priced at £5.49 in the hope that shoppers won't be wise to the fact that it is relatively poor value.

It's true that there are some wines on supermarket shelves priced at £3.29, £3.79 etc. But these price points occur with suspicious irregularity, and suggest that an awful lot of wines are being pushed the greater distance towards the next 49 and 99 pence points.

Price can be a poor guide to quality even at the best of times. The only means by which any of us can determine a wine's value is on personal taste. The ideal bottle is one you like very much and would buy again at the same price without demur.

But just for curiosity's sake, it's fun to know what the wine itself actually costs, and what the retailer is making on it. This is how the costs break down in a French wine costing £4.49 at a supermarket. This is a slightly unusual purchase by a supermarket, because the wine is being bought direct from the vineyard where it was made. Usually, retail multiples buy their wines by a less-strenuous method, from agents and distributors in the UK.

Price paid by supermarket to supplier in France for the bottled wine	£1.40
Transport and insurance to UK	£0.28
Excise duty	£1.16
Cost to supermarket	£2.84
Supermarket's routine mark-up at 30%	£0.85
VAT at 17.5% on marked-up price	£0.65
Provisional shelf price	£4.34
Adjustment in price/VAT to price point	£0.15
Shelf price in supermarket	£4.49

The largest share of the money appears to go to the producer in France. But from his £1.40 he must pay the cost of growing and harvesting the grapes, pressing them, fermenting the juice, clarifying and treating the wine. Then he must bottle, cork, encapsulate, label and pack the wine into cartons. If his margin after these direct costs is 50 pence, he's doing well.

The prime profiteer, however, is not the supermarket, even though it makes a healthy £1 in mark-up. It is the Chancellor who does best, by miles. Excise duty and VAT are two of the cheapest taxes to collect and from this single bottle of wine, the Treasury trousers a princely £1.84.

Travellers to wine-producing countries are always thrilled to find that by taking their own bottles, jugs or plastic casks to rustic vineyards offering wine on tap they can buy drinkable stuff for as little as 50 pence a litre. What too few travellers appreciate is that, for the wine itself, that's about what the supermarkets are paying for it. When enjoying your bargain bottle of wine, it is interesting to reflect on the economic reality known as 'added value' – which dictates that the worthiest person in the chain, the producer, has probably earned less than ten per cent of the final price.

Wine on the web

It's not been a good year for e-commerce. Dedicated online wine companies have been disappearing with impressive regularity, and mergers among the survivors mean there is just a fraction of the number of dotcom wine names there was at the hysterical height of the click boom a mere two years ago.

There are some big dotcom wine companies now trading, notably the Virgin enterprise, but without some brick to substantiate their click, I really do worry for the future of even the best-capitalised of these e-tailers.

This year has, however, seen steady progress for existing wine merchants who are doing a bit of dotcom on the side. Queen's wine merchant Berry Bros, founded 300 years ago, has proved an unlikely leader in the market, and has boasted sales of more than a million bottles of wine from its website so far. At the other end of the scale, Waitrose.com reports steady business and, amazingly, Sainsbury's has gone into partnership with Oddbins to sell wine via the web (as well as through direct mail and press advertising) through a joint venture called the Destination Wine Company.

I have successfully ordered wine for home delivery via the web, with a first foray into Oddbins' pre-Destination site, and was impressed by the efficiency of the service. Having placed my order I received an immediate e-mail acknowledgement, then a similar acknowledgement via the post, and only a couple of days later than promised, the mixed case of wine itself.

But there were no particular advantages to buying the wine this way. I didn't get any more discount on shop prices than I would have if I'd bought my wine in person at a branch, and there was a quoted delivery charge of £4.99 (which, curiously, was not added on my credit card payment). And, of course, I had to wait about ten days for the wine.

I can see the point of buying wine by mail order (whether you place your order by post, phone, fax or via the web seems to make little difference) from a specialist who has just one premises but who has a unique range of wine, but I remain mystified why anyone would buy the usual brands – as sold by everyone from Asda to Oddbins – by any means other than popping into the nearest branch of any one of the 50 local retailers who sell it.

I rather suspect that some dotcom wines companies hope to make their fortunes by buying their wines only after they have sold them, so to speak. Because they don't have to display stock in the shop, they needn't go to the trouble and expense of paying the supplier for it, handing over the duty and VAT to Customs, and financing storage. In the virtual shop of the web, they can accept a customer's order (and perhaps the customer's money, too) before requesting the goods from their supplier (in a hell of rush, presumably) and paying the requisite duty and tax. But this leaves no scope for next-day or even next-week delivery for the customer – which rather undermines the claimed immediacy of e-commerce.

Choice is another issue. Most dedicated e-tailers have very short lists of wine, bulked out by mixed-case offers or 'bin-end sales'. It seems that it is not yet practical to display, price and annotate more than a few dozen wines on a website. But for high-street merchants and supermarkets it's another story. The chains have head-office lists of as many as 700 different wines, but can't hope to offer the whole lot in any but their very biggest outlets. On the web, however, it's no problem. A favourite wine you can find in a Co-op superstore but not in a dinky Co-op convenience shop will probably be found on the Co-op website. The price will be the same as it is in the shop, and delivery will be dependable – and free for orders worth a reasonable minimum.

How can the new e-tailers possibly compete? They have no shop window other than the web. It is not possible to buy a single bottle of wine to taste before deciding whether to go for a case or two. How can a web-only trader provide 'customer service'? A duff bottle bought from a supermarket (on the web or not) can be returned to any branch for a replacement and/or refund (yes, some supermarkets give both), but how do you return bad wine to cyberspace? There will always be lingering doubts about reliability. Will wines have been stored correctly; will delivery be guaranteed; will credit card payment to an unfamiliar e-tailer be secure?

At this stage, I cannot safely recommend shopping anywhere on the web for wine other than from the sites of well-established retailers, whether supermarkets, high-street operators like Majestic (brilliant website), or specialised independent merchants. For these retailers, of course, internet trading is little more than an extension of their existing home-delivery operations. The only difference is that their lists can be viewed on screen instead of on paper, and orders can be placed by the same credit card over the net rather than over the phone, fax or (perish the thought) in an envelope with a stamp on it.

These are still early days for internet shopping. The traditional wine trade has watched gleefully as the brazen new e-merchants have gone to the wall, but some may yet establish themselves. In the meantime, web-shoppers will be well advised to order wine only from enterprises that inspire confidence.

Cross-Channel shopping

Choosing wine at French prices is a lot more fun than trying to decipher the average wine website, but is it really worth travelling across the Channel for the sole purpose of stocking up for a few pounds less than you would pay at home? The short answer is yes. It's fun to visit France (or even, at a pinch, Belgium) and out of season it can be very cheap. High-speed ferries, catamarans and hovercraft can carry you to historic Channel ports in an hour or two for just a few pounds if you take advantage of the perpetual ticket promotions run in the national press. Discounted tickets through the Eurotunnel are never quite as cheap, but for train enthusiasts, the journey is a treat in itself.

True, there is no longer any 'duty-free' shopping on board the ferries (there never was on the trains). But as passengers on P&O Stena, SeaFrance and Hoverspeed have been discovering since the abolition of the old tax-perk two years ago, this has made no difference. You can still buy wine, spirits and other goodies on board the ships at prices that seem remarkably adjacent to those pertaining in the good old days of duty-free.

The reason for this curious continuity is that shipping companies are now buying their supplies duty-paid on the other side of the Channel – which in some cases is almost as cheap as buying those supplies on a 'duty-free' basis used to be. After all, the duty on wine in France is only 2p a 75cl bottle. In Spain, Italy and elsewhere in southern Europe, there's no duty on wine at all. VAT in France, at 20.6 per cent, is appreciably higher than the prevailing rate of 17.5 per cent here, but ferry operators are absorbing the cost.

In effect, the ships are in direct competition with the supermarkets and hideous British-owned 'wine warehouses' in the Channel ports. But ferry operators cannot hope, really, to compete with France's huge and powerful hypermarket companies. Auchan, Cora, Continent, Leclerc and other retail multiples have enormous buying power and of course very much larger premises in which to display their goods. And the car park of a major out-of-town *hypermarché* has rather more room in which to manoeuvre a groaning trolley than does the vehicle deck of a roll-on-roll-off ferry.

As explained on page 22, wine prices are dramatically lower in French supermarkets than they are in their British counterparts. But there is a dramatic gap, too, between prices in British supermarkets either side of the water. You can discover this by visiting Tesco's 'Vin Plus' branch in the immense

Cité Europe shopping centre at the Pas de Calais (near the Eurotunnel terminal) or Sainsbury's newly enlarged drinks shop next to Calais' mega Auchan supermarket.

I am much obliged to Sainsbury's for sending me a list of their wine prices on both sides of the Channel. The difference is so spectacular that I cannot resist reproducing a few of the highlights. Remember, the difference in excise duty between the two countries is £1.14 per bottle (£1.16 in UK, 2p in France), but French VAT is higher, at 20.6p per £1-worth of wine, compared to 17.6p per £1-worth in Britain. So, if duty and VAT were the only differentials, a bottle of wine valued at £2 including mark-up by a French retailer would sell for £2.44, and £3.71 in a British shop – a price difference of about 50 per cent. But as Sainsbury's own figures dramatically demonstrate, the differential is actually far greater. By the time you are reading this, these figures may well have changed in one direction or the other, but the contrasts in price do, I think you'll agree, make a lasting impression.

Wine	UK	France	Price difference
Sainsbury's Bordeaux Blanc	£3.29	£1.45	127%
Sainsbury's Claret	£3.99	£1.75	128%
Muscadet	£2.79	£1.25	124%
Sainsbury's Anjou Blanc	£2.99	£1.25	139%
Sainsbury's Liebfraumilch	£2.89	£1.10	162%
Sainsbury's Moselle 1.5cl	£5.95	£2.10	185%
Sainsbury's Sicilia Red	£2.99	£1.05	185%
Viña Albali Reserva	£4.49	£2.25	100%
Sainsbury's Aus Chardonnay	£3.99	£1.95	105%
Sainsbury's Mendoza Red	£3.29	£1.25	163%

These differences are astonishing – and far in excess of anything accounted for by mere differences in tax. But Sainsbury's is still nothing like as cheap as some of the local retailers in Channel ports, where very drinkable vin de pays can start at as little as 6FF (1 euro), or 60 pence at around the current exchange rate.

And the fact is that it is infinitely more exciting to shop in the French *hypermarchés* than it ever can be to take the cautious route into just another Sainsbury or Tesco. Just about everything in French supermarkets is cheaper – not just the wine, spirits and beers – and there is a choice of fresh and preserved foods, in the larger superstores, that puts our own supermarkets to shame. English is widely spoken, and bi-lingual signs are commonplace in the stores.

And if you're using an appropriate credit card, paying the bill is no more complicated than it is in a supermarket at home.

There is no limit to the quantity or value of goods you can bring back from any EU member country, provided it is not intended for resale in the UK. British Customs & Excise long ago published 'guidelines' as to what they consider are reasonable limits on drinks that can be deemed to be for 'personal consumption'. You can thus import, no questions asked, 90 litres of wine, 20 of fortified wine, 10 of spirits and 110 of beer. That's about as much as a couple travelling together (and therefore able to import twice the above quantities) could cram into a family car without threatening the well-being of its suspension.

Savings on beer and spirits are, if anything, even more dramatic than they are on wine. French duty on beer is 5p a pint, compared to 33p here. This means a case of beer typically costing £12–£15 here can be had for under a fiver in Calais. It seems crazy. Similarly, a 70cl bottle of London gin or Scotch whisky costing £11–£12 here is yours for £7–£8 in France, where duty on spirits is half the £5.48 charged here and mark-ups lower.

As if these differentials were not enough, the Channel ports also teem with good-value restaurants and hotels. Boulogne and Calais, Dieppe and Dunkirk bristle with venues where you can enjoy a 100-Franc (£10–15) menu of a standard that would set you back several times as much at home. And there are respectable hotels where a clean room with bath or shower, plus croissants and excellent coffee for breakfast, can be had for £25 all in.

Why are wines so much cheaper in French shops?

The price gaps between the big stores either side of the Channel are, as illustrated above, by no means entirely accounted for by the difference between UK excise duty and VAT and French duty and VAT. So what's going on?

It's not that British supermarkets set higher margins than their continental counterparts. The Office of Fair Trading's Competition Commissioner last year absolved (some sections of the press said 'whitewashed', but I couldn't possibly comment) supermarkets of overcharging customers. But when it comes to wine, the differential between the same wine on sale in the Asda at Coventry and the Auchan at Calais arises from *how* those respective supermarkets apply their margins.

It goes like this. In France, retailers typically mark up wines at 30 per cent. In the UK, as it happens, retailers also mark up by around 30 per cent. The difference is that shops in Britain add the mark-up not to the basic value of the wine, but to the duty paid and delivered (DPD) price.

In the UK, every bottle of still wine, regardless of quality or price, comes with an excise duty and shipping cost of around £1.40. So a bottle of wine the retailer buys for £1 from the producer has a DPD price of £2.40. Marked up by 30 per cent for the retailer's margin, that becomes £3.12. Add VAT at 17.5% and the actual retail price turns into £3.66.

In France, it's different. The typical duty and shipping cost in the price of a bottle of French wine is 12p. So the DPD price of the £1 bottle is £1.12. Marked up by 30 per cent it becomes £1.32. Add French VAT at 20.6 per cent and the actual retail price is £1.59. That's more than £2 less than the price of the same bottle of wine on our side of the Channel.

The difference is inflated because British retailers charge their 30 per cent on the DPD price rather than on what they've paid to the producer. As well as paying the extra shipping cost plus the £1.10 differential between UK excise duty (£1.16) and French (2p) you're paying a further 38p of retailer mark-up.

The pick of the year

Below are the wines that have scored highest for value among the hundreds recommended in the following pages:

Red wines

10/11

Côtes de Nuits Villages, Domaine Gachot-Monot 1997	£9.95	*Irma Fingal-Rock*
Inycon Syrah 2000	£4.99	*Sainsbury's, Tesco*
Miranda Rovalley Ridge Petit Verdot 2000	£5.99	*Tesco*

10

Beaujolais, Domaine Aucoeur 2000	£6.70	*Roger Harris*
Beaujolais, Cave de St Vérand 2000	£6.05	*Roger Harris*
Beaujolais-Villages, Domaine de Franc-Pierre 2000	£6.25	*Roger Harris*
Bright Brothers Barrica Shiraz 1999	£6.99	*Sainsbury's, Somerfield*
Calvet Reserve 1998	£5.99	*Co-op, Sainsbury's, Tesco, Thresher*
Château Beauchêne Châteauneuf du Pape 1999	£9.99	*Waitrose*
Côte de Beaune Les Mondes Rondes, Domaine Michel Poulleau 1998	£7.95	*Irma Fingal-Rock*
Good Ordinary Burgundy 1999	£4.99	*Safeway*
Le Monstre Grenache Noir 2000	£4.99	*Tesco*
Mont Gras Carmenère Reserva 2000	£5.99	*Sainsbury's, Waitrose*
Safeway Cabernet Sauvignon Vin de Pays d'Oc 2000	£3.99	*Safeway*
Somerfield Vin de Pays des Coteaux de l'Ardèche 1999	£2.99	*Somerfield*
Tatachilla McLaren Vale Grenache-Shiraz 2000	£7.49	*Majestic*
Tesco Finest Corbières Reserve La Sansoure 2000	£3.99	*Tesco*
Valréas Domaine de la Grande Bellane 1999	£4.99	*Co-op*
Vision Merlot Reserve 2000	£7.99	*Tesco*

White wines

11/12

Waldracher Krone Auslese, Peter Scherf 1989	£5.99	*Majestic*

10/11

Bernkasteler Graben Riesling Kabinett 1999	£6.99	Tesco
Erdener Treppchen Spätlese, CH Berres, 1994	£5.99	*Majestic*
Inycon Chardonnay 2000	£4.99	*Co-op, Safeway,*
		Sainsbury's, Somerfield, Tesco, Waitrose

10

Alsace Gewürztraminer Beblenheim 1999	£9.99	*Majestic*
Bonterra Chardonnay 1999	£8.49	*Oddbins, Thresher*
Bourgogne Vézelay Le Clos, Domaine Elise Villiers 1998	£7.85	*Irma Fingal-Rock*
Catena Agrelo Vineyards Chardonnay 1999	£8.99	*Waitrose*
Charleston Pinot Gris 2000	£6.99	*Waitrose*
Château Carsin Cuvée Prestige 1998	£7.59	*Waitrose*
Isla Negra Chardonnay 2000	£4.99	*Tesco*
Jordan Chardonnay 2000	£7.99	*Waitrose*
Kaseler Kehrnagel Riesling Kabinett, Bert Simon, 1990	£4.99	*Majestic*
Mehringer Zellerberg Auslese, Weingut Dahmen-Kuhnen 1998	£5.99	*Majestic*
Neethlingshof Gewürztraminer 2000	£5.99	*Oddbins*
Ockfener Bockstein Riesling Kabinett, State Domaine Trier 1992	£4.49	*Majestic*
Riesling QbA, Friedrich William Gymnasium, 1991	£3.99	*Majestic*
Stoneleigh Vineyard Sauvignon Blanc 2000	£6.49	*Waitrose*
Tesco Finest Great Southern Riesling 2000	£5.99	*Tesco*
Urziger Würzgarten Spätlese, CH Berres, 1993	£5.99	*Majestic*
Villa Maria Private Bin Riesling 2000	£5.99	*Waitrose*

The retailers

In this edition, I have focused attention on the largest national retailers. The 'big five' of Asda, Safeway, Sainsbury's, Somerfield and Tesco are here in depth. So is Waitrose which, in spite of confining its shops so strictly on a geographical basis (namely England's high-earning southern regions), has easily the widest and most-exciting range of any of the supermarkets – and offers the entire list to mail-order customers nationwide.

I have not included regional supermarkets (Waitrose aside) or high-street merchants, because none offers very much, if anything, that cannot be found in the nationwide chains. National high-street retailers Thresher-Wine Rack-Victoria Wine and Oddbins are here, as is the admirable 'warehouse' network of Majestic Wine.

There are two small-scale merchants included, not just to strike a balance with the huge retailers that take up most of this book, but to illustrate that specialist merchants with a nationwide home-delivery service can offer as much, if not more, in terms of quality and value as the biggest national multiples.

A diverse collection of retailers, and a wide world of delicious wine, all of which, in their different ways, I heartily recommend.

ASDA

During the summer of 2001 I made two forays to Asda stores to view the range and buy some 'samples'. Even in the larger of two branches, the choice of wines seemed very limited, and I could not help noticing the shelf space was more taken up by the ubiquitous brands – Jacob's Creek, Gallo and so on – than I remember from visits in previous years.

Now that Asda is part of the world's biggest retailer, Wal-Mart, I suppose I expected to find more interesting, individual wines and of course masses of own-labels. But the fact is that the range continues to represent a fraction of the choice in the other members of the Big Four, Safeway, Sainsbury's and Tesco.

The own-label wines I brought home for tasting were more mixed for quality and value than I had expected – some were excellent in both respects and are mentioned here with due enthusiasm. But a few from among the cheapest own-labels were poor, and while I have refrained from listing them here with sub-6 scores, I must say they have left me cautious about recommending Asda as a positive choice for shoppers who put wine high on their list of priorities when it comes to choosing a supermarket.

Among the many well-known brands at Asda, this warm, ripe and peppery Gascon red, costing £4.99, stands out.

ARGENTINA

£3.79 9/10 Asda Argentinian Bonarda 1999 *Delicious bramble-nosed soft but trim Italian-style spaghetti wine at a very good price*

£3.99 7 Asda Argentine Sangiovese 2000 *Does have a certain nutty bite, but rather dilute*

£4.49 8 Far Flung Cabernet Merlot 2000 *Plenty of blackcurranty concentration and grip*

£4.97 9 Rio de Plata Cabernet Sauvignon 1996 *Amazing to find this still on shelf, it's a delicious mature, silky red still drinking well in relative old age*

£4.99 9 Argento Malbec 2000 *Dark, dense and liquorous wine by excellent Nicolas Catena – needs food*

£5.99 9 Cafayate Cabernet Sauvignon 1998 *Give this a try – it's a smooth but nicely edged mature wine with a minty appeal*

AUSTRALIA

£3.49 9 Asda Karalta Shiraz Cabernet 2000 *Not as vividly fruity as the 1999 vintage but still a good, round glassful at this price*

£3.99 9 Mighty Murray Red 2000 *Dubious name but a very decent jam-scented middleweight (though 14% alcohol) food wine at a keen price*

CHILE

£2.99 9/10 Asda Tramontane Red 1999 *Very cheap but a completely formed and balanced ripe red with southern warmth*

£4.99 9 Buzet Cuvée 44 1998 *I keep coming across this brand, and keep liking it – warm and ripe with peppery hint*

£4.99 8 Terramater Zinfandel Shiraz 2000 *Soft-fruit style delivers beguiling mix spice and strawberry*

£5.88   9   Louis Jadot Beaujolais Villages 2000   *Burgundy négociants Jadot are a reliable source of Beaujolais – this one is plump and juicy and worth the money*

ITALY
£2.77   9   Asda Sicilian Red 2000   *Tastes just the same as all other supermarket own-label red Sicilians and as such, good, and even cheaper than most*

£3.47   8   Trulli Primitivo del Salento 2000   *Light in colour but dark in intense fruit – food wine*

£3.99   9/10   Asda Chianti Colli Senesi 2000   *Very successful indeed – concentrated mocha-and-cherry style with lively fruit, grippy finish*

£4.99   8   Pendulum Zinfandel 1999   *Gilt-bottled Puglian plummy-raisiny winter wine*

PORTUGAL
£4.79   8   Cataplana 1999   *A light (but 13.5% alcohol) and squishy-minty red-fruit glugger from the Algarve*

Amazingly cheap for the quality – a soft and spicy blend with a finely edged finish.

WHITE WINES

ARGENTINA

£2.99   9   Asda Argentinian White

Very cheap soft 'tropical-fruit' dry white is a respectable party wine

£3.49   9/10   Asda Argentinian Torrontes 2000

Whiff of spicy-grapy Muscat about this fruit-salad of a wine

£4.97   9   Far Flung Viognier 1999

Nice weight to this peachy soft but refreshing dry white with 13.5% alcohol

AUSTRALIA

£3.62   9   Asda Karalta Semillon 2000

Cheaper than last year's vintage and about as good – distinct peachy-honey nose on a dry fresh fruit

£4.49   9   Lindemans Cawarra Unoaked Chardonnay 2000

Cleverly contrived big brand has purity and creaminess and impressive citrus finish

£4.99   9/10   Cranswick Estate Marsanne 1999

Exotic aroma to this gold-coloured pineapple-and-vanilla confection

£4.99   9   Garnet Point Semillon-Chardonnay 2000

Chardonnay dominates in a rather subtle (and just 11.5% alcohol) minerally and apple crisp dry wine

£4.99   9   Pendulum Chardonnay 1999

'Concept' wine in a weird silvered bottle, looks a lot better in the glass – generous gold colour and rich vanilla-coconutty style

£5.97   9   Houghton's HWB 1999

Lush combo of Chardonnay and Sauvignon, is very big seller in Australia where HWB stands for Houghton's White Burgundy but little seen here – give it a try

CHILE

£4.79 9/10 35 South Sauvignon Blanc 2000   *Very fresh, almost briny, aroma and crisp, tangy style to this well-priced refresher*

£4.99 9 Undurraga Gewürztraminer 2000   *Nothing like the Alsace version but this is still an exotic and perfumed off-dry white of character*

FRANCE

£4.99 9 Denis Marchais Hand-Picked Vouvray 1999   *Blossomy nose on this lush but zesty Loire dry white*

£6.99 9/10 Asda Chablis 2000   *Cheap Chablis – and £6.99 is fairly cheap – is usually anonymous stuff but this own-label is excellent: pebbly-fresh, pretty good weight, and genuinely in the classic Chablis style*

GERMANY

£3.92 8 Kendermann Riesling Kabinett 1999   *Rightly popular brand is crisp and, I suppose, appealingly un-German*

£3.99 9 Devil's Rock Riesling 2000   *Looks Australian but this racy Rhine wine is crisp, dry and definitely German*

ITALY

£3.99 9 Asda La Vis Pinot Grigio 2000   *Like last vintage, an aromatic, smoky style with easy fresh softness – a cut above most cheaper PGs*

£4.29 9 Marc Xero Chardonnay   *Creamy-fruit dry style comes in a frosted bottle*

SPAIN

£3.87 10 Asda Manzanilla Sherry   *Absolutely cracking value – a tangy ultra-dry sherry to compare with brands at twice the price*

PERSONAL NOTES:

....
....
....
....
....
....
....

BOTTOMS UP

See Thresher

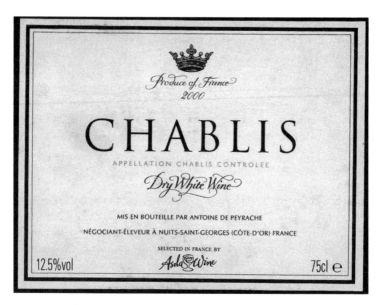

Excellent value for money – the Classic Chablis style at £6.99.

CO-OP

The 1,840 co-op shops and superstores within the organisation known since 2001 as the Co-operative Group – a union of the formerly distinct Co-operative Retail and Co-operative Wholesale societies – now sell wines from a common range. And a very impressive range it is, too.

Even the little convenience stores, such as the one in my Somerset home town of Castle Cary, have a useful choice of brands and own-labels, and every month feature a new collection of special offers that frequently lop substantial percentages off the featured wines.

Compared to the wines in rival shop chains Londis and Spar, the Co-op is miles better, far more interestingly sourced and a clear winner on price. Even with the major supermarkets, the Co-op stands comparison perfectly well.

In the last year, the Co-op has come up with some interesting new wines. First, amidst much ballyhoo, was the launch of the 'first "Fair Trade" wine to go on sale in Britain'. Following the established trend for fair-trade groceries including bananas and coffee, the Co-op is proud to say that this breakthrough wine is made by the Los Robles growers' co-operative in Chile's Curico Valley where membership 'guarantees the farmers a fair price for their grapes and the additional funds generated from this fairly traded wine, which also includes a social premium, will help boost productivity by improved production techniques'.

Next development has been along similar lines, with the boosting of the Co-op's choice of organic wines by the addition of four new French own-label vins de pays. These, 'all approved by Ecocert, the French organic certifying body', followed the new, smartly-labelled series of vins de pays introduced earlier in the year.

Quality is consistent throughout these new wines, and price pretty steady, too – all under £5.

The Co-op has its own dedicated website for wine shoppers who prefer home-delivery. It gives details of current special offers as well as 'a selection' from the full list of 500-or-so different wines and spirits: www.grapeandgrain.co.uk.

ARGENTINA

£3.69 9 Co-op Argentine Malbec-
Bonarda 1999

Good value Italian-style own-brand has bright flavours and neat finish – good for drinking with pasta

£3.99 9/10 Adiseño Tempranillo 2000

Cheerfully vanilla-flavoured blackcurrant essence is formulaic, but friendly

£3.99 8 Graffigna Shiraz-Cabernet
Sauvignon 1999

Slightly tough blend, just as apparently overripe as the previous vintage, so the style is presumably intended

£3.99 9 Lost Pampas 2000

Co-op own-brand has edgy-young, glyceriney style from Cabernet and Malbec grapes

£4.99 9 Argento Malbec 2000

Dark, dense and liquorous wine by excellent Nicolas Catena – needs food

AUSTRALIA

£4.99 9 Lindemans Cawarra Shiraz
Cabernet 2000

Decent spicy wine is light by Oz standards but satisfying

£5.99 8 Lindemans Bin 50 Shiraz 1999

Toasty-spicy wine has been hiked 20% in price since last year – still good but not such good value

£5.99 7 Brown Brothers Tarrango 1999

Pale and juicy light red holds together pretty well, but doesn't excite

£6.99 9 Rosemount Shiraz Cabernet 2000

Juicy and spicy berry-fruit dark style is relishably brambly

CHILE

£3.79 5 Long Slim Red Cabernet-Merlot

Thin and stringy wine camouflaged under an eyecatching label

£3.99 8 Four Rivers Cabernet Sauvignon
1999

Strong, distinctly blackcurranty and slightly tough

£4.99	8	Co-op Fair Trade Chilean Carmenère 2000	*Decent middleweight blackcurranty wine is made by fair-trading Los Robles co-operative*
£4.99	8	Terramater Malbec 1999	*Direct punchy dark fruit is uncomplicatedly pleasing*
£4.99	8	Terramater Zinfandel-Syrah 2000	*Soft, sweetish style evokes strawberries – and white pepper*

FRANCE

£3.99	9/10	Co-op Vin de Pays d'Oc Cabernet Sauvignon	*One of an impressively consistent new range of vin de pays introduced in 2001, this is well-balanced between sturdiness and juiciness with lush cassis fruit*
£4.99	9	Co-op French Organic Merlot Syrah	*Neat marriage of silk and spice in this ripe vin de pays from the new organic range*
£4.99	10	Valréas Domaine de la Grande Bellane 1999	*Intensely ripe and spicy top-of-the-range organic Côtes du Rhône Villages at a great price*
£5.99	10	Calvet Reserve 1998	*Brilliant Bordeaux brand has wet-cellar-floor nose with cassis bubbling up from below – a balanced middleweight claret of unaccustomed quality in this price range*

ITALY

£2.99	9	Co-op Sicilian Red Wine	*As cheap as it comes, a friendly cherry-topped red of real charm*
£4.99	9/10	Inycon Merlot 1999	*Nice spearmint waft off this handsomely coloured Sicilian wine with dark, peppery fruit – gripping stuff with 14.5% alcohol*

| **£4.99** | 9 | Melini Chianti 1998 | *Light-ish but firm fruit with the proper nutskin-dry finish and an evocative cherry whiff in a big-brand Chianti that's unusually good value for money* |
| **£5.49** | 9 | Otto Santi Chianti Classico 1998 | *Reasonable price for this cherry-fruit and grippy Chianti with plenty of concentration* |

PORTUGAL

| **£3.29** | 9 | Ramada 2000 | *Whiff of clove oil and honey-minty centre to the lightweight fruit – an intriguing cheapie from Estremadura region* |
| **£3.99** | 9 | Terra Boa 1999 | *Sweet nose but keenly edged dark fruit to this workmanlike red from Tras-Os-Montes region* |

SOUTH AFRICA

| **£4.99** | 9 | Goats do Roam 2000 | *Gimmicky name echoes Côtes du Rhône and wine has vibrant, bouncy fruit* |

SPAIN

| **£3.99** | 9 | Berberana Dragon Tempranillo | *Rather a good, cheap oaky middleweight from a famed Rioja producer* |
| **£4.49** | 8 | Viña Albali Tinto Reserva 1995 | *Emphatically vanilla-oaked mature Valdepeñas is light-ish but satisfying* |

USA

| **£3.99** | 6 | Laid Back Ruby 2000 | *Lured into this gaudy Californian 'ruby Cabernet' only to find it a rather dilute confection* |

ARGENTINA

£3.99 9 Rio de Plata Torrontes 2000   *Grapy-soft but breezily crisp aperitif wine or Asian-food matcher*

AUSTRALIA

£3.99 7 Butterfly Ridge Sauvignon-Chenin Blanc 2000   *Cheap fresh lightweight for parties*

£4.49 9 Hardy's Stamp Series Chardonnay-Semillon 2000   *Catch-all big-brand blend delivers clean Chardonnay with a mild caramel twist – really rather likeable*

FRANCE

£3.99 8 Co-op Vin de Pays Chardonnay-Chenin Blanc   *Safe, soft dry white is 'vegetarian'*

GERMANY

£3.69 8 Co-op Four Rs 1999   *New wave (i.e. un-Liebfraumilch-like) grapy-fresh dryish white*

£3.99 9 Devil's Rock Riesling 2000   *It's German, but not as we know it – appley-crisp Riesling to refresh and stimulate*

HUNGARY

£3.29 7 Co-op Hungarian Chardonnay 1999   *Bargain-priced method wine is light and inoffensive – go for 2000 (untasted) for freshness*

ITALY

£4.49 9/10 Trulli Chardonnay 1999   *Encouraging rich colour and a blast of appley-oily perfume on this Salento (heel of Italy) varietal – the 2000 vintage, not tasted, will be worth chancing*

£4.99 10/11 Inycon Chardonnay 2000

OK, it's a popular brand – just about all the supermarkets now have it – but this Sicilian masterpiece by the huge Settesoli co-operative is just great: gold colour, fresh, appley classic Chardonnay nose (no oak involved), heaps of ripeness (14% alcohol) and flavours sublimely orchestrated into a beginning, a middle and an end

PORTUGAL

£4.99 8 Fiuza Chardonnay 2000

Dried-fruit note in this unusual rich but dry Chardonnay

PERSONAL NOTES:

. . . .

. . . .

. . . .

. . . .

. . . .

. . . .

A fruity Chianti with an evocative cherry aroma, unusally good value at £4.99.

ROGER HARRIS WINES

Based at a farm in Norfolk, Roger Harris is Britain's leading quality-retailer of the wines of Beaujolais. It's a narrow specialism, certainly, but a valuable one – because most of the Beaujolais on sale in this country, through the supermarkets, is dull stuff unworthy of the name.

This is why I am including this small firm amongst the big chains. It's quite simple: if you want good Beaujolais, don't expect anything interesting or fairly priced from a supermarket. With few exceptions, the wines on the big chains' shelves are from négociants who buy grapes or wine from an assortment of different producers and blend them together for labelling with a brand name.

Real Beaujolais, with the distinctive juicy liveliness and purity characteristic of the Gamay grape, the sole variety used for the red wines, is the kind made by vinegrowers and co-operative members who make the wine themselves and take a pride in the distinctiveness of their efforts.

These are the kind of producers who populate Roger Harris's list. He knows them all – he's been buying wine in their region for 25 years – and he'll deliver to your door, wherever you live, the best of this great region's wines.

Prices are about £1.50 higher for the Beaujolais AC and Beajolais-Villlages AC wines compared to what you'll pay in a supermarket, but you're getting a different kind of wine altogether. For the grander wines, the ten ACs that go under the name of particular villages, Harris's prices are pretty much the same as the supermarkets – and the wines, of course, are in a different league.

To balance up the domination by red wines of his splendid annual list, Roger Harris also imports some commendable whites from the neighbouring Mâconnais region.

Roger Harris is a wholesaler so the minimum order is 12 bottles, which can be any mix. Delivery is very efficient indeed in my experience. Place an order before 12 noon on a working day, and you can expect to receive the wine the following day. Orders worth £150 or more are delivered free; there is a £3 charge for orders valued below £100; and £2 for orders between £100 and £150.

Roger Harris Wines, Loke Farm, Weston Longville, Norfolk NR9 5LG. Tel 01603 880171. Fax 01603 880291. Website: www.beaujolaisonline.co.uk.

FRANCE (Beaujolais)

£6.00	9	Beaujolais-Villages, Cave du Château de Chénas, 2000	*Delicious light but perfectly ripe wine – refreshing drunk moderately chilled*
£6.05	10	Beaujolais, Cave de St Vérand, 2000	*Purply-bright, violet and summer-fruit-redolent lightweight with grip as well as bounce – unfiltered wine that can throw a healthy deposit*
£6.25	10	Beaujolais-Villages, Domaine de Franc-Pierre, 2000	*Dark, intense and flamboyantly ripe with a flavour that bursts in the mouth in a way no other wine can match*
£6.35	9/10	Beaujolais AC, Domaine de Milhomme, 2000	*Lush and exuberant 'basic' Beaujolais has concentrated colour, cherry-ripe nose, lively fruit with terrific grip*
£6.50	8	Beaujolais, Blaise Carron, 2000	*Unusual abrasive quality and notable acidity to this solid, rustic specimen*
£6.70	10	Beaujolais, Domaine Aucoeur, 2000	*Structured and gloriously ripe as well as joyously juicy and simply delicious*
£6.90	9	Beaujolais-Villages, Manoir du Pavé, 2000	*Purple colour and taste – vibrant fruit and emphatic refreshing acidity, delicious with a starchy dish involving haricot beans*
£7.35	9/10	Régnié, René Desplace, 1999	*Concentrated lipsmacking wine with tight-knit sweetly ripe fruit*
£7.50	9	Chénas, Domaine de Maupas, 1999	*Tight fruit and concentrated style, definitely a food wine – which will evolve well over the next year or two*
£7.75	9	Moulin à Vent, Cave du Château de Chénas, 1999	*Gripping but softly ripe wine is still quite young-tasting but by no means too young to drink now*

£8.15	9/10	Fleurie, Caves des Producteurs des Grands Vins de Fleurie, 1999	*Pure silk – soft, rounded and rich yet with the brisk acidity of the best-made wines*
£8.20	9	Brouilly, Château Thivin, 2000	*Sweetly ripe and pure-tasting young wine of great character*
£8.45	9/10	Côte de Brouilly, Château Thivin, 2000	*Lovely bright colour and thrillingly perfumed with everything from overripe Victoria plumskins to squished blackberries – silky and luxuriant*

WHITE WINES

£7.35	8	Mâcon Milly Lamartine 2000	*Sturdy but zestily fresh Chardonnay has fleshy appeal and long finish*
£8.10	9	Beaujolais Blanc, Lucien Charmet, 1997	*A rare bird, this peachy and rather rich Chardonnay is very well balancedwith freshness and limey acidity*
£8.65	9	Viré Clessé, Jean Noël Chaland, 1999	*Grapefruit-scented minerally-plump elegant Chardonnay*

PERSONAL NOTES:

. . . .

. . . .

. . . .

. . . .

. . . .

. . . .

. . . .

. . . .

. . . .

. . . .

IRMA FINGAL-ROCK

Irma Fingal-Rock is the name of a food and wine shop in Monmouth, Wales. I discovered this remarkable emporium in 2001 by making the acquaintance of its owner, former London barrister Tom Innes, who started the business 15 years ago and whose wonderful range of wines is now available nationwide by mail order. Because he provides this service, his wines are arguably as accessible as those of Asda or Tesco – and a lot of Tom's wines, it has to be said, offer considerably better value than anything the major supermarkets have to offer.

But what is of really special interest about Irma F-R (so-called after Mrs Innes's maiden name) is the extraordinary list of Burgundies, nearly all of which Tom obtains by the radical method of travelling to the region, visiting the people who make the wines, tasting them in their homes and cellars, choosing what he wants and then bringing them home.

Tom Innes might have trained for the law, but I swear that until he started dealing in wine he had missed his vocation, because he has a knack for finding great Burgundies at affordable prices. And this is a very rare knack indeed. Sure, supermarkets and off-licences sell Burgundies at under a tenner, but they are almost invariably rubbish. And yes, the grandest wine merchants do sell delicious Burgundies – but at astronomical prices.

Fifteen years after his first foray into Burgundy, Tom Innes takes pride in specialising in wines from small individual producers, and in pricing them fairly. 'My prices are sharp,' he says with disarming frankness. 'I know I have to compete to stay alive.' By buying so many of his wines direct from the growers, he's cutting out agents and UK distributors – and he's passing on the benefit to customers, both local and mail order, on whose loyalty he so crucially depends.

For most of us who love Burgundy but cannot afford simply to buy the big names year after year, a merchant like Innes is a godsend. So fragmented are the region's vineyards that finding the true-value wines of real quality is almost impossible. Tom Innes himself doesn't claim to find it easy. 'Even the best growers have their ups and downs,' he says.

But he does follow a core of favourite growers, with Domaine Gachot-Monot at the top of the list. Tom does buy a limited amount of wine from négociants, including Louis Latour, but his list, featuring so many diverse names and a good range of vintages (plenty of mature wine here), will gladden any Burgundophile's heart.

I have tasted just a small sampling of the hundred-or-so Burgundies on offer (about half are under £10) and describe these below, but the real point of this entry is to encourage all *Best Wine Buys* readers with an interest in Burgundy to send for the list, and investigate it for yourself.

Elsewhere, there's a good spread from other bits of France and around the world. The right names crop up with encouraging regularity: Daniel Jarry Vouvray, Alain Graillot Crozes, Gaja in Piedmont, Louis Guntrum among the Germans, Henschke in Australia. Even the sherries are spot-on – he's cottoned on to that well-kept secret among finos, Williams & Humbert's incomparable Pando.

This enterprise definitely merits a visit or at least a phone call for a copy of the list. Delivery is free within a 30-mile radius of Monmouth and in central London, and elsewhere depending on the route that day of the Fingal-Rock van – otherwise by carrier at cost or free if your order exceeds £100.

Irma Fingal-Rock, 64 Monnow Street, Monmouth NP25 3EN. Tel 01600 712372. E-mail irmafingalrock@msn.com. Website: www.pinotnoir.co.uk.

FRANCE (Burgundy)

£5.95   9   Bourgogne Passetoutgrain, Gachot-Monot, 1999

Young leafy vivid red from a blend of Gamay and Pinot Noir grapes

£7.95   10   Côte de Beaune Les Mondes Rondes, Domaine Michel Poulleau, 1998

Classic Burgundy at a giveaway price – it's still young and eagerly gripping but already laden with insinuating summer fruit and will improve for years

£8.98   9/10   Hautes Côtes de Beaune, Jean et Geno Musso, 1999

Pure strawberry whiff of this pleasantly edgy organic red – profound enough to warrant a bit of ageing but already delicious

£9.95   10/11   Côtes de Nuits Villages, Domaine Gachot-Monot, 1997

Lovely limpid village Burgundy of pure, earthy quality for now and for at least the next ten years – the best red Burgundy I have tasted at under £10 in many years

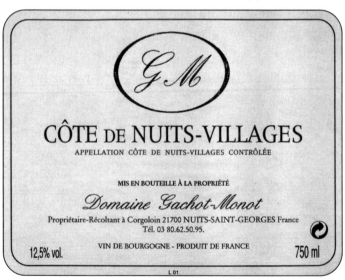

Delicious grower's burgundy at under £10 is a rarity, so this lovely limpid red at £9.95 from Irma Fingal-Rock is a real find.

FRANCE (Burgundy)

£7.35	9	Petit Chablis, Domaine Dennis Pommier, 1998	*Well-coloured, minerally and brisk wine of real character – by no means a 'small' wine*
£7.85	10	Bourgogne Vézelay Le Clos, Domaine Elise Villiers, 1998	*Sensational with a fleeting but unmissable fresh-lime-juice whiff, then a pebble-bright entry and lush heart with some creamy evidence of oak and wonderfully integrated*
£7.88	9/10	Chablis Domaine Jean-Marie Naulin 1998	*Fresh and vigorous Chablis aspiring to the grand premier cru style and utterly delicious*

PERSONAL NOTES:

. . . .

. . . .

. . . .

. . . .

. . . .

. . . .

. . . .

. . . .

. . . .

. . . .

. . . .

. . . .

. . . .

MAJESTIC

Majestic seems to be prospering mightily, increasing sales at something like 15 per cent per annum. In the last financial year, their sales reached an impressive £86 million. It's good to see a wine-selling operation other than a supermarket that is doing really well.

Founded 20 years ago, with a single site in Battersea, Majestic now has 95 branches around the country, and, says the company, 'it is hoped we will reach the important milestone of our 100th store by the end of the year'.

The top-scoring wine of the year with 11/12, this sublime moselle has a spice and diesel nose, apples, minerality, honey finish and racy freshness – all for £5.99 at Majestic.

As an independent company, with many of its own employees among the shareholders, I greatly admire Majestic. It's big enough to buy wine (and beer and spirits) at the best rates but small enough to entertain the wines of small-scale producers – thus, for example, the fantastic collection of wines from Germany and all sorts of individual producers from France, Italy and beyond.

Majestic do endless promotions on great numbers of wines, mostly of the 'multibuy' variety, in which you qualify for a discount if you buy two or more bottles. For once, this kind of promo makes sense, because Majestic being a wholesaler, you have to buy at least 12 bottles (mixed or otherwise) anyway.

I do recommend that a trip to Majestic to make that bulky purchase needs forward planning. Bear in mind that the average spend by a Majestic customer per visit is £102. So try to get hold of the current list (a bulky 36 colour pages) beforehand, or look up the website at www.majestic.co.uk and plan what you're interested in. I do buy wine occasionally from my nearest Majestic (in Bristol) and always kick myself if I haven't made an advance note of what I'm looking for – because it can be difficult to find everything you want among the canyons of cartons.

I rate Majestic as high as any of the mass retailers, and I think their prices are very fair.

ARGENTINA

£6.99 9/10 Carrascal Cavas de Weinert 1997 *Still a youthful purple colour in spite of its age, this dark-heart red from Malbec, Cabernet and Merlot grapes has startling similarity with a decent claret – and a good claret at that*

AUSTRALIA

£3.49 9 Coldridge Estate Shiraz Cabernet 2000 *Remarkably cheap for a decent Aussie red – plenty of sunny fruit*

£5.99 9 Noble Road Shiraz 1999 *Comparative lightweight (a mere 13% alcohol) among Majestic's Oz reds but has a likeable eucalyptus-scented, keenly edged fruit*

£6.49 8 Bethany Barossa Valley Grenache 1999 *Pale coloured but a massive (14.5% alcohol) mouth-coating hotly ripe spicy red to suit the macho palate*

£6.49 9 Oxford Landing Limited Release Shiraz 1998 *Easy-drinking, deeply flavoured spicy style – 13.5% alcohol*

£6.99 9/10 Ironstone Margaret River Shiraz Grenache 1998 *A friendly giant (14.5% alcohol) with redcurrants and soft jamminess in a plush texture*

£7.49 10 Tatachilla McLaren Vale Grenache-Shiraz 2000 *Gorgeous squashed-fruit nose on this crushed-bramble, lavishly ripe (14.5% alcohol) smoothie*

£8.99 9/10 Kangarilla Road McLaren Vale Cabernet Sauvignon 1999 *So dark it's nearly black, this gripping wine is intensely blackcurranty, ripe (14% alcohol) and unnervingly akin to a five-year old, good-quality Bordeaux*

CHILE

£4.79 7 Vistasur Cabernet 1999 *Everyday red, seems a bit hard-edged*

£4.79 7 Vistasur Merlot 2000 *Ordinary soft-fruit red, is a shade woody*

£5.99	9	Valdivieso Barrel Selection Merlot 1999	*Keen cutting edge to this vividly fruity red – will go very well with starchy dishes*
£6.49	8	Casa Lapostolle Cabernet Sauvignon 1999	*Dense purple colour, wet nose and mouth-drying tannin but a likeable-enough wine that might improve with time*
£6.99	8	Santa Rita Reserva Cabernet Sauvignon 1999	*Firm middle fruit in a classic cassis red – simple wine, perhaps a bit pricy*
£6.99	9	Santa Rita Reserva Merlot 1999	*'Full-bodied' would for once be a fair description of this generous, sweet-cherry, firm-finishing ripe (14% alcohol) and lingering red*
£8.99	9	Valdivieso Single Vineyard Reserve Cabernet Franc 1999	*Subtle purply mouth-gripping wine has good balance of ripe fruit and dry edge*

FRANCE

£2.79	9	Domaine de Richard 2000	*This Vin de Pays de l'Aude seems astoundingly cheap – plenty of sunny fruit for the money*
£4.99	7	Beaujolais Villages, Georges Duboeuf, 1999	*Fair effort from the 'King of Beaujolais' but the wine's not as uplifting as the famous floral label*
£4.99	9	Costières de Nîmes, Château Guiot, 2000	*Ripe (13% alcohol) and concentrated purple warm-fruited spicy red – good value, typical of the appellation*
£5.49	9	Corbières, Château de Luc, 1999	*Rounded and smooth with a white-pepper tinge*
£5.49	9	Chinon Les Garous, Couly-Dutheil, 1999	*Characterful leafy densely fruity vigorous Loire red*
£6.99	6	Brouilly, Georges Duboeuf, 2000	*Beaujolais brand is no more interesting than everyday Villages*
£6.99	9	Château Pech Redon La Clape 1999	*Dark ripe smoothie from the Languedoc has warm summery fruit*

£6.99	8	Château du Trignon Côtes du Rhône Villages Sablet 1999	*Pale slightly woody but well-focused upmarket CDR, 13.5% alcohol*
£7.49	9	Morgon Jean Descombes, Georges Duboeuf, 2000	*Nice raspberry nose and sunny fruit from a Beaujolais cru that's still a bit young*
£7.99	8	Alsace Pinot Noir Beblenheim, Bott-Geyl, 1999	*Very pale, spicy dry red tending towards leanness, but good of its kind*
£8.99	9	Château Robin 1998	*From the Côtes de Castillon, one of Bordeaux's humbler outreaches, a purple-bright, young blackcurranty midweight claret of real character*
£8.99	9	St Joseph, Domaine de Rochevine, 1997	*Handsome but still beetroot coloured (and hint of beetroot on the nose, too) northern Rhône classic is still a little austere – one to keep a couple of years*
£8.99	9	Sancerre Rouge, Domaine Fournier, 1998	*Pinot Noir has a flinty edge readily associable with brisk style of the better-known Sauvignon whites of Sancerre – a fine, firm cherry-strawberry scented red*
£9.49	8	Gigondas, Château du Trignon, 1999	*Pale-coloured but strong (14% alcohol) spicy and concentrated Rhône village red – not cheap, though*
£9.99	9/10	Châteauneuf du Pape Clos St Marc 1996	*Wine of this famous name has lately become very expensive but this meadow-scented, orangey-hued, fruit-basket example is good value*
£9.99	9	Sancerre Rouge, Laloue, 1999	*Another gripping Pinot Noir with a delicious mineral style*

ITALY

£2.99	6	Sangiovese di Pasqua 2000	*Sweet ersatz nose and pale, even anaemic fruit – principal attraction is the cheapness*
£4.99	7	Cabernet Sauvignon del Montello, Vengazzu, 1998	*All-purpose Cabernet of Veneto, NW Italy*
£4.99	8	Col di Sasso, Banfi, 1999	*Sleek Chianti-style wine from huge American-owned estate in Tuscany has cherry fruit*
£4.99	9	Copertino Masseria Monaci 1998	*Good solid wine with an earthy – even volcanic – element and proper Italian dry finish*
£4.99	9/10	Sangiovese Syrah, Accademia del Sole Calatrasi, 1999	*Velvety colour, spirity-raisiny nose, generous earthy fruit and nutskin finish on this delightful Sicilian, made by an Australian*
£5.49	9/10	Rosso Conero Conti Cortesi 1998	*Earthy berry-fruit southern red has appreciable grip and peppery ripeness – this kind of wine benefits from decanting*
£5.99	6	Santa Cristina Antinori 1999	*Rather dilute vintage for this famous wine from leading Chianti producer Antinori*
£6.99	9	Dogajolo Carpineto 1999	*Wonderful label on this friendly, cherry-and-cinnamon Tuscan – great pasta-party red*
£6.99	9	Selian Carignan Tunisia Calatrasi 1999	*Made in Sicily with grapes shipped from Muslim Tunisia by its Australian maker, a dark, minty, softly tannic red of real charm*
£7.49	9/10	Valpolicella Classico Superiore Ripasso La Casetta de Ettore Rignetti 1998	*Emphatic fruit lingers in the mouth as long as the name lingers on the lips – bright, intense, almondy wine of great character and 13.5% alcohol*

£7.99	8	Chianti Classico Banfi 1998	*Cherry-scented pleasantly abrasive Chianti is good, but seems rather expensive*
£7.99	9	Montepulciano d'Abruzzo Vigne Le Coste Cornacchia 1998	*Deep dense purply colour and creamy texture, lots of supple fruit – an ingratiating upmarket wine*
£9.99	9	Rosso di Montalcoholino Banfi 1997	*Pricy but delicious mature heavyweight has tarry depths and lush plummy fruit – special wine*

NEW ZEALAND

| £8.99 | 9 | Delegats Reserve Cabernet Sauvignon 1999 | *Typical minty Kiwi nose and sleek, silky cool-climate character – this classic New Zealand is distinctive and delicious* |
| £8.99 | 8 | Delegats Reserve Merlot 1998 | *Very dark and dense, ripe (14% alcohol) liquorice fruit and plenty of tannin – needs time* |

Sleek Chianti-style wine from an American-owned estate in Tuscany.

ARGENTINA

| £5.99 | 9 | Alamos Chardonnay 1999 | *Lush nutty-tangy and inspiringly interesting wine from top Argentine producer Nicholas Catena* |

AUSTRALIA

£3.49	9	Coldridge Estate Chardonnay 2000	*Cabbagey nose but a cleverly contrived lot of fruit and 13.5% alcohol – plenty of interest at a rarely low price for Australian wine*
£4.49	9/10	Tatachilla Breakneck Creek Chardonnay 2000	*Loads of colour, intriguing green-wood nose and a lot of flavour for the money*
£5.49	9/10	Barossa Valley Riesling, Bethany, 2000	*Alluring appley-spirity nose and the limey-fresh fruit follows up – very good value for such a lot of interest*
£5.99	9	Oxford Landing Limited Release Viognier 2000	*Certain apricot, lychee and green-leaf character to a nicely nuanced softly dry white*
£5.99	9	Tatachilla McLaren Vale Sauvignon Semillon 1999	*Lively floral nose and zippy fruit from the grape varieties with which dry white Bordeaux is made – rarely with this sort of panache*
£6.49	8	Ironstone Semillon Chardonnay 1999	*Honey hint of Semillon grapes marries pleasantly with appley Chardonnay to crisp effect – not cheap, though*
£6.49	8	Tatachilla McLaren Vale Chardonnay 2000	*Great big rich middle fruit in this sunny item – and 13.5% alcohol*
£7.99	8	Kangarilla Road Chardonnay 2000	*Eye-catching label on a decent wine, but rather pricy*

| £9.49 | 9 | Cape Mentelle Semillon Sauvignon 2000 | *Much-praised producer's blend is Sauvignon dominated with lots of brine and gooseberry – masses of fruit and ripeness (13.5% alcohol) and great concentration* |

CHILE

£4.79	8	Vistasur Sauvignon 2000	*Simple direct fresh fruit*
£6.49	6	Santa Rita Reserva Sauvignon 2000	*Famous estate's Sauvignon is not as exciting as before – rather flat*
£6.99	9	Casa Lapostolle Chardonnay 1998	*Splendidly over-the-top golden super-ripe Chardonnay*

FRANCE

£2.99	9	Cuvée de Richard Vin Blanc	*Bog-standard non-vintage vin de table lacks pretension but is fresh and stacked with crisp fruit – a really dependable party plonk*
£3.99	9	Vin de Pays des Côtes de Gascogne, Vivian Ducourneau, 2000	*Bright clean fruit with a grapefruit note – an attention-grabbing wine*
£4.29	8	Sauvignon Les Chapelières 2000	*Gently abrasive Vin de Pays d'Oc has plenty of fruit*
£4.49	8	Muscadet Sur Lie, Château La Touche, 2000	*Rather a soft, but pleasantly tangy, variation on the usually sharply acidic theme*
£5.49	7	Laroche Grande Cuvée 'L' Chardonnay 1999	*Oaky New World-style Vin de Pays d'Oc*
£5.99	9	Vouvray Demi-Sec, Domaine Bourillon d'Orléans, 1999	*Unfashionable Loire is softly honeyed, just off-dry, and makes a delicious aperitif*
£6.49	8	Quincy, Jean-Charles Borgnat, 2000	*Fresh, but not overcrisp, Sauvignon from the Loire*
£6.49	9	Reuilly, Henri Beurdin, 2000	*Interesting custard whiff off a crisp dry Sauvignon with a lush twang – quality wine*

£7.99	9	Sancerre Chavignol, Paul Thomas, 2000	*Generous flinty gooseberry fruit in this refresher*
£8.49	7	Sancerre, Domaine Laloue, 2000	*Positively prickly-fresh style – might be a bit challenging for the shyer palate*
£8.99	9	Alsace Pinot Gris, Bott-Geyl, 1999	*Well-coloured, soft and smoky wine of real character*
£8.99	9/10	Sancerre La Guiberte, Alain Gueneau, 2000	*Gorgeous stony-but-rich wine with complexity, length and lovely crisp finish*
£8.99	9/10	Sancerre Les Boucards, Claude Riffault, 2000	*Another lush wine, full of fresh grassy fruit and with a pebbly edge – not cheap, but an experience*
£9.49	10	Alsace Gewürztraminer, Beblenheim 1999	*Gorgeous gold colour, classic lychee nose, a big rich wine with crisp finish and classic aftertaste*
£9.99	8	Sancerre Vieilles Vignes Domaine Fornier, 2000	*Minty-vanillin note to this luxury* **wine** – *delicious but untypical*

GERMANY

£3.99	10	Riesling QbA, Friedrich William Gymnasium, 1991	*Can't be much of this miraculous bargain left, but it's still listed – a perfect petrolly mature Moselle of real quality (10% alcohol)*
£4.49	9	Bockenheimer Grafenstück Beerenauslese 1998 half bottle	*Pink-tinged stickie is rather like a rich Muscat but has cleverly contrived clean acidity*
£4.49	10	Ockfener Bockstein Riesling Kabinett, State Domaine Trier, 1992	*Highly coloured, crisp and extraordinarily lively Moselle for its age – delightful and just 8% alcohol*
£4.99	10	Kaseler Kehrnagel Riesling Kabinett, Bert Simon, 1990	*Rush of racy fruit and crunchy acidity, merest suggestion of diesel, 8.5% alcohol, limey fresh in spite of decade in bottle*

£5.99	10	Mehringer Zellerberg Auslese, Weingut Dahmen-Kuhnen, 1998	*Not sweet as expected, just a shade of lemon-blossom honey amidst the crisp, lush fruit which takes a positive grip on the tastebuds – fabulous wine*
£5.99	10/11	Erdener Treppchen Spätlese, CH Berres, 1994	*Pure gold – hint of botrytis honey deep in the nose of this limpid Moselle which is nevertheless wonderfully crisp, fresh and lemon-edged – and just 7.5% alcohol*
£5.99	10	Urziger Würzgarten Spätlese, CH Berres, 1993	*Honeyed but racy, weighty but only 7.5% alcohol, sweet-appley yet crisply citrus finish*
£5.99	11/12	Waldracher Krone Auslese, Peter Scherf, 1989	*Bright, even luminescent gold colour, spice and diesel nose, apples, minerality, honey finish and racily fresh right through – the barest hint it's already 12 years old*

ITALY

£6.99	9/10	Pinot Bianco Alto Adige, Alois Lageder, 2000	*Heavenly floral smell, zippy smoky-spicy fruit and weighty mouthfeel to this Alpine refresher*
£6.99	8	Pinot Grigio Toscana, Banfi, 2000	*Crisp and nicely smoky PG from huge American-owned winery in Tuscany*
£8.49	7	Gavi di Gavi Late Picked Villa Lanata 2000	*Famed Piedmont off-dry white is rich and interesting, but rather expensive*

NEW ZEALAND

£5.99	8	Villa Maria Private Bin Riesling 2000	*Flinty style, still seems a bit closed up – needs time to unfold?*

SPAIN

£6.99	7	Rioja Blanco, Muga, 2000	*New-Worldised dry white tastes more like herb-flavoured oaked Chardonnay than indigenous Rioja – quite nice, though*

ODDBINS

Winner every year of the International Wine Challenge's 'Wine Merchant of the Year' award ever since I can remember, Oddbins is the darling of the wine press. The chain is certainly one of the most written about, although recently the coverage has consisted largely of speculation about Oddbins' corporate future. The business, as part of drinks multinational Seagram, is due for 'disposal' as Seagram gets out of booze (its new boss prefers media and movies) and it has been rumoured that a major supermarket might buy the chain.

Front runner – and this is pure, unfounded speculation – is Sainsbury's, which in 2001 entered a business arrangement with Oddbins to create a co-operative mail-order and internet (www.tasteforwine.co.uk) enterprise called the Destination Wine Company. Their retail operation has been christened Taste for Wine after the Taste name used by Sainsbury's with another of its business partners, Carlton, for their food-and-drink TV channel.

The point of the Taste for Wine joint venture almost entirely eludes me, as it sells wines you can already buy in Oddbins and/or Sainsbury's branches, but you have to buy them a dozen bottles at a time, paying £4.99 for home delivery if you order just one case, although delivery is free if you order two or more cases.

The service is advertised in the national press and is featured in a number of the respective retailers' branches. The wines on offer at discounts are sold as mixed cases, with perks such as a free 13th bottle if you order a case of 12 bottles. Otherwise, there's a big list of wines available – set to reach 750 lines in all – from which you can pick and mix your own selections.

What fascinates me about all this is that these two leading retailers think it's such a great idea to encourage the public in general, no doubt including millions of their own existing customers, to shop from home instead of getting out to their respective stores. It might be that the scheme is designed to encourage wine shoppers to spend more – the wines on offer are nearly all priced at £5-plus – or it may be they think this way they can grab back some business from already-successful mail-order enterprises such as Laithwaite's (Bordeaux Direct), the Wine Society and really competent internet operators such as Majestic and Waitrose.

Good luck to them, I say. But if Taste for Wine, whose lists so far have been of perfectly ordinary branded wines – mostly available from many more retailers than merely Oddbins and Sainsbury's – at not particularly advantageous prices, manages to pay its own way in the foreseeable future I will be very surprised indeed.

Back to the point. If you're interested in Oddbins' wines, you're unlikely to be very far from a branch – there are around 250 of them throughout the country – and they are certainly among the most interesting wine shops anywhere, with staff who are uniquely informed and attentive. Oddbins tends to be associated with good champagne prices and lots of 'New World' wines, but curiously enough, I don't think either of these features are to be counted among their strengths. There are better deals on champagne to be found elsewhere, and Australian and American wines do not improve by way of proliferation. I think the most interesting wines in Oddbins come from France, especially the Midi, Italy and elsewhere in the Olde Worlde.

I certainly recommend a visit to an Oddbins branch rather than a click on their one-dimensional tasteforwine website. After all, you can buy just one bottle at a time if you appear in person, and if you do want to buy a mixed case, you'll get a decent discount and very likely a hand to your car with it.

Note that Oddbins' own website, www.Oddbins.com, is still in operation, and that in addition to the nationwide network of shops they have one in Calais, too, offering the same stock at moderately reduced prices: Oddbins Cité Europe, 139 Rue de Douvres, 62902 Coquelles Cedex. Tel 00333 21 82 07 32.

ARGENTINA

£4.99	9	Argento Malbec 2000	*Dark, dense and liquorous wine by excellent Nicolas Catena – needs food*
£6.99	9	Fabre Montmayou Malbec 1998	*Rather sophisticated variation on the usual leathery theme of this grape – dense and dark, but lush*
£7.99	9	Ricardo Santos Malbec 1999	*Extravagant dense smoothie has a raisiny, dark-chocolate centre fruit – leaves a lingering impression*

AUSTRALIA

£4.99	8	Deakin Estate Shiraz 2000	*Upfront red berry fruit, a simple glugger*
£4.99	9	Lindemans Cawarra Shiraz Cabernet 2000	*Decent spicy wine is light by Oz standards but satisfying*
£5.99	8	Lindemans Bin 50 Shiraz 1999	*Toasty-spicy wine has been hiked 20 per cent in price since last year – still good but not such good value*

CHILE

£3.99	9/10	Quiltro Cabernet Sauvignon 1999	*Cheerful cheapie has the sort of ripeness that only Chile can do at this sort of price*
£4.99	9	Viña Porta Cabernet Sauvignon 1999	*Reliable budget Cabernet has meatiness and grip as well as authentic blackcurranty ripeness*
£6.49	9	Errazuriz Cabernet Sauvignon 1999	*Gripping muscular red has 13.5% alcohol and concentrated cassis fruit – should just be at peak maturity in 2002*
£8.99	7	Errazuriz Reserve Cabernet Sauvignon 1988	*Famous producer's top red is rather formulaic; good but not that good*

FRANCE

£3.99 9 Mosaique Syrah 1999 *Good-value spicy ripe Vin de Pays d'Oc*

£3.99 8 Ptomaine des Blagueurs 1997 *Leafy, manageably abrasive strong Vin de Pays d'Oc*

£5.99 9/10 Château Grand Escalion 1998 *Excellent-value Costières de Nîmes has intensely ripe blackberry-and-vanilla fruit – a treat*

£6.99 9 James Herrick Millia Passum 1998 *New(ish) brand from famous Languedoc Chardonnay producer has lush Syrah fruit with weight and grip*

£7.49 9/10 Château de Nages Cuvée Torres 1998 *Top-of-the-heap Costières de Nîmes is muscular without being tough, and is delectably spicy*

£7.49 9 Rasteau, Chapoutier, 1999 *Gripping quality Rhône has years ahead of it, but is already darkly delicious*

NEW ZEALAND

£9.99 9 Montana Pinot Noir Reserve 1999 *New Zealand Pinot Noirs have a distinctive minty, eucalyptus style and density of character that makes them completely distinct from their Burgundy counterparts – this one is an excellent example*

PORTUGAL

£4.99 9 Bela Fonte Baga 1999 *Dark hint of coffee in this keenly berry-fruit quality red*

SOUTH AFRICA

£4.99 9 Goats do Roam 2000 *Gimmicky name echoes Côtes du Rhône and wine has vibrant, bouncy fruit*

SPAIN

£4.29 9/10 Taja Jumilla 2000   *Very good value from the Alicante region, a soft but sinewy wine*

USA

£6.49 9 Redwood Trail Pinot Noir 1998   *Perennial favourite from California is brimming with sunny strawberry-raspberry aromas and flavours*

£6.99 9 Fetzer Valley Oaks Cabernet Sauvignon 1998   *Rich, spirity nose gives way to a gently ripe and deliciously squishy easy-drinking wine*

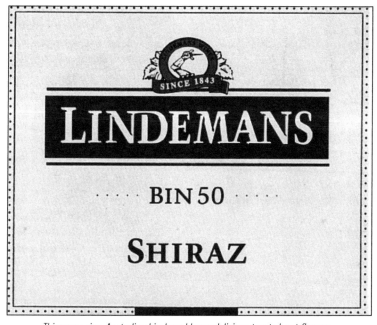

This super-ripe, Australian big-brand has a delicious toasted-nut flavour.

AUSTRALIA

£4.99 9 Wynns Coonawarra Riesling 2000 *Florally scented limey-fresh mineral wine of character*

£6.29 9 Antipodean Unoaked Chardonnay 2000 *Chardonnay without the influence of oak has become a cult and the good ones have palpable purity as well as lushness – this qualifies*

CHILE

£5.99 9 Trio Gewürztraminer 2000 *Yet another good lychee-perfumed spicy-exotic aperitif wine from the grape made famous by Alsace*

FRANCE

£3.99 8 Kiwi Cuvée Sauvignon Blanc 2000 *Loire Valley attempt at replicating the zing and zap of New Zealand Sauvignon is only moderately successful – but cheaper here than elsewhere*

£4.49 9 Sieur de Camandieu Vignier 2000 *Typical peach and apricot nose on a well-priced lightweight Vin de Pays d'Oc*

£4.99 9 James Herrick Chardonnay 1999 *Australian-owned Vin de Pays d'Oc has dependable mineral character*

£5.29 9/10 Pinot Blanc Cuvée Reserve, Cave de Turckheim, 2000 *Nifty Alsace has herbaceous, exotic depths and clean citrus acidity*

GERMANY

£7.49 9/10 Armand Riesling Kabinett 1999 *Epic wine of a style more reminiscent of Australia than of its Pfalz origin where it is made by top grower von Buhl – florally perfumed and crisp*

GREECE

£4.99   9   Gaia Notios 2000

Oddbins specialises in Greek wines, and this fresh dry softie is a good introduction – no resemblance to Retsina

ITALY

£3.99   9   Il Padrino Grecanico-Chardonnay 2000

Successful Sicilian blend has zest and interest

£4.69   9/10   Trulli Chardonnay del Salento 2000

Just in, another lusciously complex vintage of this pineappley-exotic dry white

NEW ZEALAND

£5.99   9   Montana Unoaked Chardonnay 2000

Appetising pure-fruit shardy from NZ's biggest winery has zest and concentration

£7.99   9   Montana Reserve Marlborough Chardonnay 1999

Luxury wine has gold colour and enough rich fruit to justify the price

PORTUGAL

£4.99   9   Bela Fonte Bical 1999

Crisp but attractively complex dry white

SOUTH AFRICA

£5.99   10   Neethlingshof Gewürztraminer 2000

A Cape tilt at Alsace's most-exotic wine is a real hit – crisper than the French style, but with no concession to lychee aroma and exotic spice, and competitive in price

SPAIN

£5.99   9   Cosme Palacio y Hermanos 1998

White Rioja has the vanilla creaminess of old but also the clean-acidity freshness of the new – impressive

USA

£6.49 8 Beringer Sauvignon Blanc 1998 *Unusually weighty style has Sauvignon's gooseberry brightness but also an underlying richness – interesting*

£7.99 8 Fetzer Viognier 1999 *Peachy example of this popular genre is delicious but pricier than some rivals*

£8.49 10 Bonterra Chardonnay 1999 *A personal favourite, this organic Californian has extraordinary purity*

PERSONAL NOTES:

....

....

....

....

....

....

This floral-limey dry Australian white has impressive weight and definition of flavour.

SAFEWAY

Rather in keeping with their name, Safeway seem to have opted for caution as far as their wines are concerned. There were few interesting new introductions on show at their annual press tasting in the spring, but the familiar wines still look pretty good.

There have been a lot of changes among the people who buy the wines for Safeway, and this might explain the innovation gap. Once a new team is well established perhaps we can look forward to the sort of excitement that prevailed when Liz Robertson MW, who left in 1999, was at the helm.

Safeway, along with all the other supermarkets, eagerly embraced the internet craze a couple of years back to 'e-tail' their wines. But they don't seem to have had much joy with their own website, and in 2001 joined up with a specialised e-tailer called madaboutwine.com to launch safewaywinesdirect.co.uk. This offers customers a 'facility to shop for value-for-money, quality wines online from home or the office, putting the pleasure back into buying wine with the bonus of a delivery service'. That delivery is promised within five days, and online shoppers in London can opt for evening delivery – so they can be in when the van calls.

AUSTRALIA

£4.99 8 Jindalee Merlot 2000
Medicinal cherry smell but nicely integrated fruit

£5.49 9 Tatachilla Breakneck Creek Cabernet Sauvignon 2000
Purple-black, red-berry fruit, soft and jolly glugger – fun wine

£5.99 9/10 Wakefield Promised Land Shiraz-Cabernet Sauvignon 2000
Heaps of blackberry fruit with a leathery top-note but softly gluggable – stands out from the crowd

£5.99 9 Wirrega Vineyards Shiraz 1999
Agreeable roasted flavour to this old-fashioned hearty Shiraz with a good cutting edge of acidity

£9.99 8 Alkoomi Shiraz 1999
Dramatically dense purple colour and plush, spicy fruit

BULGARIA

£3.49 6 Safeway Young Vatted Cabernet Sauvignon 2000
Sweet, home-winemaking-kit style of wine

£3.49 5 Safeway Young Vatted Merlot 2000
Not as good as remembered in earlier years, this lacks the 'velvet' claimed on the label and has a disturbing acetone smell

CHILE

£4.49 8 Morande Syrah 2000
Round, plausible, sweet-bottomed wine is pleasant and unusually low in alcohol at 11.5%

£4.99 9 Cono Sur Cabernet Sauvignon 2000
Vivid blackberry nose on this young, eager wine with soft immediacy

£4.99 7 Valdivieso Malbec 2000
Surprisingly light example from a grape that tends to make dense, dark wine in Latin America

£6.99	8	Santa Rita Cabernet Sauvignon 1999	*Unusually tough and tannic for a Chilean, this well-concentrated red may improve with keeping*
£9.99	9/10	Valdivieso Single Vineyard Cabernet Franc 1998	*Velvety ripe smooth-oaked wine with leafy background flavours – rather expensive but worth it*

FRANCE

£2.99	8	Safeway Corbières 2000	*Cherry stone flavour about this light-middleweight makes for easy drinking*
£2.99	9	Safeway Minervois 2000	*Deep but bright purple colour and a good grip to this ripe (13% alcohol) cheapie*
£3.99	9	L'Enclos des Cigales Merlot 2000	*Summer-fruit Vin de Pays d'Oc has fleshy ripeness and comforting weight*
£3.99	10	Safeway Cabernet Sauvignon Vin de Pays d'Oc 2000	*This one hits the spot – perfectly ripe sunny blackcurrant fruit has ideal ratio of cassis sweetness to crisp crunch*
£4.99	8	Bourgueil Les Chevaliers 2000	*Pale vigorous Loire red with strawberry-leafy smell and pleasant edgy fruit*
£4.99	10	Good Ordinary Burgundy 1999	*From the great co-operative at Buxy in the Chalonnais region, this is true southern Burgundy – pale but tightly-knit young wine with cherry nose and sweet-but-true young fruit; tastes like Pinot Noir, but is actually Gamay*
£4.99	8	La Source Merlot-Syrah 2000	*Deep purple-coloured wine from famed Domaines Virginie in Languedoc has a stalky note but vivid concentrated fruit*
£4.99	8	Anciennes Vignes Carignan 2000	*Upfront oak-influenced 'bistro' wine of sunny quality*

£4.99	9	Château Villespassans, St Chinian, 2000	*Purple-black, hedgerow-fruit, gripping finish*
£5.49	8	Château Salitis, Cabardes, 1998	*Maturing Languedoc red has big, ripe New World-type fruit but still lots of mouth-puckering tannin – fun to keep a couple of years to await developments*
£5.99	9/10	Château Bouisset Cuvée Eugenie, La Clape, 2000	*Enticing crème de cassis richness to this dense-purple deeply concentrated Languedoc red – long, lingering flavours*
£5.99	9	Mourvèdre-Grenache, JL Denois, 1999	*Vivid raspberry fruit in a nicely rounded Vin de Pays d'Oc – good value*
£6.99	9	Vacqueyras, Domaine de la Bouscatière, 1999	*Buy this Rhône village wine for keeping – it will reward patience as its 14% alcohol, opulent weight and emerging spicy fruit overcome the present mouth-puckering tannin*
£8.99	9	Château Teyssier, Montagne St Emilion, 1998	*Cool, minty, still-immature but exciting claret from one of St Emilion's 'satellite' appellations – needs more time, ideally*
£9.99	9	Safeway Beaune 1998	*Whiff of white pepper on alluring raspberry nose of this young-tasting burgundy – delicious firm fruit that will develop for at least a couple of years*

ITALY

£4.49	9	La Nature Nero d'Avola 2000	*Ripe, heathery Sicilian with good concentration*
£4.99	9	Canaletto Nero d'Avola Merlot 2000	*Big mouthful of warm spicy fruit from Sicily*

NEW ZEALAND

£9.99 9 Montana Pinot Noir Reserve 1999 *New Zealand Pinot Noirs have a distinctive minty, eucalyptus style and density of character that makes them completely distinct from their Burgundy counterparts – this one is an excellent example*

SPAIN

£4.99 8 Siglo 1881 1999 *Pale, orange-hued colour and roasted style speak of a very hot harvest – this is interesting stuff*

£9.99 7 Marques de Murrietta Reserva Tinto 1997 *Colour going orange and a spirity, vanilla nose on this grand Rioja, but not enough interest for the money*

USA

£3.99 7 Pacific Coast Ruby Cabernet 2000 *A sort of Californian Beaujolais Nouveau*

£5.99 9 Pepperwood Grove Syrah 1999 *Densely coloured and, yes, detectably peppery ripe red with good heart – a true food wine*

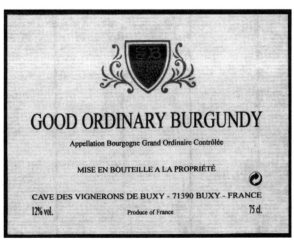

Straightforward name and an honest bargain is Safeway's own-label burgundy at £4.99 – tightly knit flavours from an excellent co-operative producer.

AUSTRALIA

£7.99 8 Alkoomi Sauvignon Blanc 2000 *Real rush of grassy-fresh flavour in this upmarket refresher from Frankland River, Western Australia*

£8.99 9 Tatachilla Adelaide Hills Chardonnay 1999 *Clever mix of mineral freshness and soft, agreeably custardy richness – a grand, golden wine*

CHILE

£4.79 9/10 Aresti Gewürztraminer 2000 *Pleasing pale-gold colour and a proper whiff of lychee to this crisp and delicious imitation of the classic Alsace style – and much cheaper than the original*

£4.79 9/10 35 South Sauvignon Blanc 2000 *Very fresh, almost briny, aroma and crisp, tangy style to this well-priced refresher*

£9.99 9 Casa Lapostolle Cuvee Alexandre Chardonnay 1999 *Pricy but deliciously opulent wine fermented in 'new French oak Burgundy barrels' is a bargain by Burgundy standards*

FRANCE

£3.99 7 Sauvignon Cuvée Réserve 2000 *Softer variation on the grassy Sauvignon theme from Languedoc*

£3.99 7 Touraine Sauvignon 2000 *Crisp and fresh everyday Loire dry white*

£3.99 9/10 Viognier Cuvée Réserve 2000 *Generous exotic dried-fruit smell and mouthfilling off-dry fruit in this good-value Vin de Pays d'Oc*

£4.99 9 Domaine La Tour du Marechal Chardonnay 2000 *Organic Vin de Pays de l'Hérault has yellow colour, caramel-tipped nose and easy ripe fruit*

£5.99 8 Domaine de Bosquet Chardonnay 2000 *Method coconutty oaked Vin de Pays d'Oc is in the Australian style*

£5.99	8	Safeway Gewürztraminer 2000	*Rather a sweet style to this lychee-perfumed Alsace wine*
£5.99	8	Via Domitia Chardonnay-Viognier Réserve Spéciale 2000	*Substantial soft oaked Vin de Pays d'Oc*
£6.99	3	Domaine de Ciffre Viognier 2000	*Dirty and sour – a bad bottle, one hopes*
£8.99	8	Sancerre Bonnes Bouches 2000	*Pricy but deliciously lush and zesty Sauvignon from reputable producer Henri Bourgeois*
£9.99	9	Safeway Pouilly Fuissé 2000	*Flinty freshness and creamy weight combine to make a delicious, if expensive, Chardonnay*

GERMANY

| £3.99 | 7 | Langenbach St Johanner Spätlese 2000 | *Soft, grapy commercial hock* |

HUNGARY

£2.99	6	Safeway Irsai Oliver 2000	*Soft, grapy one-dimensional dry white has cheapness as principal merit*
£3.79	8	Riverview Chardonnay/ Pinot Grigio 2000	*Quite sweet but fresh and lively and a likeable drift of smokiness – well priced*
£4.29	7	Riverview Gewürztraminer 2000	*Typical canned-fruit style of the exotic Gewürz grape but rather sweet*
£4.29	8	Riverview Sauvignon Blanc 2000	*Breezy, near-salty nose but a soft, low-acidity fruit to this glugger*

ITALY

£4.99 10/11 Inycon Chardonnay 2000

OK, it's a popular brand – just about all the supermarkets now have it – but this Sicilian masterpiece by the huge Settesoli co-operative is just great: gold colour, fresh, appley classic Chardonnay nose (no oak involved), heaps of ripeness (14% alcohol) and flavours sublimely orchestrated into a beginning, a middle and an end

NEW ZEALAND

£7.99 7 Grove Mill Riesling 2000

Late-harvested grapes and incomplete fermentation leaving residual sugar makes this an interesting, but rather expensive, off-dry style

£8.99 9 Delegats Barrique Fermented Chardonnay 1999

Extravagant oaked style with memorable lingering afterflavours

£9.99 9 Villa Maria Sauvignon Blanc Reserve 2000

Lashings of gooseberry fruit and a certain profundity in this top-flight Marlborough wine – nice hint of residual sweetness

PERSONAL NOTES:

. . . .

. . . .

. . . .

. . . .

. . . .

. . . .

. . . .

. . . .

. . . .

SAINSBURY'S

What is Sainsbury's wine department up to? In 2001 they've launched into a joint venture with Oddbins to sell wine through direct mail, press advertising and – inevitably – the internet. Why would a company presumably anxious to promote its own name in what is a desperately competitive business allow its priceless corporate image to be tangled up with a maverick, even faintly anarchic, outfit like Oddbins?

It can only be, I suppose, that supermarkets on Sainsbury's scale by now feel they have grabbed so much of the take-home wine market (about three-quarters of it between them) that if they want to take the other quarter they'll have to cosy up to the likes of Oddbins, and by offering certain blandishments, steal their customers.

Well, good luck to them. Meanwhile, Sainsbury's seem to have made surprisingly few improvements or extensions to their own range of wines in the last year. To my great sorrow I missed their early-summer press wine tasting this year, but visits to the stores and a perusal of their list lead me believe they are continuing to fall behind Tesco and Waitrose for choice and value.

Big-brand wines, from the impressively dull relaunched Piat d'Or wines to the ubiquitous Blossom Hill, Gallo, Paul Masson of California, seem to take up more and more space on the shelves. And while the Australian range runs to more than 80 different items, I reckon there are probably only half a dozen producers responsible for the lot of them.

It's the mass-retailer's *modus operandi* in the 21st century: buy big from very big companies with generous promotional budgets (which fund not just national advertising but also the endless discounts and multibuy offers on their brands), and if there's no space left on the shelves for individualistic wines, then too bad.

Choice, I would say, is the loser. I hope Sainsbury's will start looking a bit further for their wines, but I'm not holding my breath.

ARGENTINA

£4.49 9 Santa Julia Bonarda
Sangiovese 2000

Good-value crisply bright middleweight has the keen-fruit style of young Chianti

£4.99 9 Argento Malbec 2000

Dark, dense and liquorous wine by excellent Nicolas Catena – needs food

£6.99 10 Bright Brothers Barrica Shiraz
1999

Top-of-the-range dark, dense and silky vanilla-toned monster (14% alcohol) has sweet lushness but nicely trimmed dry finish

£8.99 9/10 Catena Cabernet Sauvignon 1997

Fabulous wine with the 'cigar box' whiff of posh claret, and packed with silky cassis fruit

AUSTRALIA

£5.49 9 Tatachilla Breakneck Creek
Cabernet Sauvignon 2000

Purple-black, red-berry fruit, soft and jolly glugger – fun wine

£5.99 9 Lindemans Bin 45 Cabernet
Sauvignon 2000

Good black-fruit easy-drinking brand has, regrettably, gone up in price by 25 per cent this year

From Portugal's Tras-Os-Montes region, this is a mature-tasting but lively red.

CHILE

£4.79 9 Valdivieso Cabernet Sauvignon 2000
Crunchy-briary fruit in this sleek quenching red

£4.99 8 Terramater Zinfandel Shiraz 2000
Soft-fruit style delivers beguiling mix of spice and strawberry

£5.99 10 Mont Gras Carmenère Reserva 2000
Top-class intensely concentrated berry-ripe red has silky mouthfeel

FRANCE

£2.99 8 Sainsbury's Cabernet Sauvignon 1999
Serviceable Vin de Pays d'Oc is ripe and complete – and cheap

£3.29 9 Sainsbury's Côtes de Roussillon
Bit of a bargain, this – spicy, even peppery, fruit with lots of grip

£4.99 9 Côtes du Rhône Villages, Domaine Bernard, 2000
Nicely constructed peppery-leafy wine from yet another great vintage in the Rhône

£5.99 10 Calvet Reserve 1998
Brilliant Bordeaux brand has wet-cellar-floor nose with cassis bubbling up from below – a balanced middleweight claret of unaccustomed quality in this price range

£5.99 9/10 Valréas Domaine de la Grande Bellane 1999
Intensely ripe and spicy top-of-the-range organic Côtes du Rhône Villages

ITALY

£2.99 9/10 Sainsbury's Sicilia Red
Very cheap for such a characterful aromatic and warmly spicy lightweight red

£3.99 8 The Full Montepulciano
Gripping sweet-centred brambly red has sufficient charm to compensate for the silly name

£3.99	9	Sangiovese di Sicilia	*Monster (14.5% alcohol) Sicilian has deceptively innocent cherry nose and bouncy fruit*
£3.99	9	Sainsbury's Montepulciano d'Abruzzo 1999	*Hedgerow fruit and lively vigour to this pasta-matcher*
£4.99	9	Emporio Nero d'Avola Merlot 1999	*Likeable dense, earthy deep-south red with lipsmacking finish*
£4.99	10/11	Inycon Syrah 2000	*Dense and dark to the point of opacity, this huge (14.5% alcohol) Sicilian has massive briary fruit with a roasty, liquorice heart – terrific value*

MOROCCO

£3.99	9	Sainsbury's Moroccan Syrah 2000	*Apparently the Moroccan wine industry is in mid-Renaissance: this is a Rhône-style silky-ripe and spicy midweight*

PORTUGAL

£3.99	9	Terra Boa 1999	*Sweet nose but keenly edged dark fruit to this workmanlike red from Tras-Os-Montes region*
£4.49	9/10	Segada Trincadeira Preta-Castelao 1999	*Love this juicy darkly spicy and minty food wine*
£5.99	9	Tinta da Anfora 1998	*Handsome minty dense black-fruit wine with vanilla oakiness*

SPAIN

£4.49	8	Alteza Tempranillo Cabernet Sauvignon 1999	*Pleasant squishy blackcurrant essence is an easy mouthful*
£4.49	8	Viña Albali Tinto Reserva 1995	*Emphatically vanilla-oaked mature Valdepeñas is light-ish but satisfying*

£4.99	9/10	Dama de Toro, Bodegas Fariña, 1998	*Dark, chocolate-hearted smoothie has a lot of velvety appeal at this price*
£4.99	9	Monte Cuervo Premium Tempranillo 1997	*Still around from last year – when it was a slinky blackcurranty number with genuine appeal*
£5.99	9	Enate Cabernet-Merlot 1999	*Chewy hot-climate blend from quality-producing Somontano region has ripeness and grip*

PINK WINES

FRANCE

| £3.99 | 9 | Big Frank's Deep Pink 2000 | *Southern Vin de Pays Merlot has sunny fruit and decent grip – don't be put off by the gimmicky presentation* |

A Sicilian masterpiece: gold colour, fresh classic Chardonnay nose.

AUSTRALIA

£4.99 9 Pendulum Chardonnay 2000

'Concept' wine in a weird silvered bottle looks a lot better in the glass – generous gold colour and good weight in the mouth

£4.99 8 Rawsons Retreat Bin 21 2000

Mango-nosed tropical mid-dry white has springy softness

CHILE

£4.79 9/10 35 South Sauvignon Blanc 2000

Very fresh, almost briny, aroma and crisp, tangy style to this well-priced refresher

£4.99 9/10 Canepa Gewürztraminer 2000

Alsace-style gem is a delicious, fresh but exotically spicy dry white with an authentic lychee whiff

FRANCE

£3.49 9 Muscat de St Jean de Minervois half bottle

Good ultra-sweet wines now rarely come as cheap as this nectareously grapy confection

£3.99 6 Old Tart Terret Sauvignon Blanc 2000

The joke really is that if it wasn't called Old Tart it would be priced at £2.99, which is about what it's really worth

£4.99 9 French Revolution 1999

From the Loire, a successful mix of soft Chenin Blanc and crisp Sauvignon Blanc – scores for refreshment value as well as interest

£4.99 8 James Herrick Chardonnay 1999

Australian-owned Languedoc is most un-Australian in character – pale, crisp and pleasantly vegetal oak-free style

£4.99	9	La Baume Sauvignon Blanc 2000	*Big-brand Vin de Pays d'Oc is consistently fresh, lively and decent value*
£4.99	9/10	Vouvray la Couronne des Plantagenets 2000	*Another lush vintage for this honey-toned but delightfully fresh, soft demi-sec from the Loire*
£5.99	7	Fat Bastard Chardonnay 1999	*Ordinary oaky Vin de Pays d'Oc that has spawned a whole genre of dismal brands with even worse names*

GERMANY

£2.39	8	Sainsbury's Liebfraumilch	*Better, fresher and livelier than branded versions at twice this price*
£3.99	9	Devil's Rock Riesling 2000	*Looks Australian but this racy Rhine wine is crisp, dry and definitely German*
£4.99	9	Kendermann Cellar Selection Riesling Spätlese 1999	*Dry Moselle has ripe grapy depths and racy fruit*

ITALY

£4.99	8	Connubio Pinot Grigio 2000	*Serviceable PG has some smoky character – above average*
£4.99	10/11	Inycon Chardonnay 2000	*OK, it's a popular brand – just about all the supermarkets now have it – but this Sicilian masterpiece by the huge Settesoli co-operative is just great: gold colour, fresh, appley classic Chardonnay nose (no oak involved), heaps of ripeness (14% alcohol) and flavours sublimely orchestrated into a beginning, a middle and an end*

£4.29 9 Marc Xero Chardonnay   *Creamy-fruit dry style comes in a*
                                            frosted bottle

PERSONAL NOTES:

. . . .

. . . .

. . . .

. . . .

. . . .

. . . .

. . . .

. . . .

. . . .

. . . .

. . . .

. . . .

. . . .

. . . .

. . . .

. . . .

. . . .

. . . .

. . . .

SOMERFIELD

'Somerfield slated as a basket case' ran the eye-catching headline in my local newspaper, *The Western Daily Press,* when the Bristol-based supermarket company was given a distinctly unenthusiastic write-up by former Lever Brothers chairman Andrew Seth in his 2001 book *The Grocers.* Seth went so far as to say: 'At the end of 2000, it was hard to believe the company would be in existence for very much longer.'

This all sounds a bit hard. True, Somerfield has slipped from fourth-largest grocer to seventh, and its takeover of the Kwik-Save chain a few years back has proved something of a burden, but these stores remain a very friendly place to shop for wine.

Somerfield have a particularly good range of own-label wines, with the vin de pays range from southern France of special note. Prices are keen, and promotions wide-ranging, with very generous discounts. Somerfield is the only place you're ever likely to find a drinkable wine at £1.99 – several of their £2.99 wines have been cut to this long-forgotten price point in promotions over the last year.

Somerfield has a website on which you can check out latest promotions and peruse the wines in general: www.somerfield.co.uk.

A concentrated coconut-oak wine from Languedoc.

ARGENTINA

£3.99	8	Somerfield Argentine Tempranillo 1999	*Light wine has briary fruit that's easy to drink*
£4.29	9	Somerfield Argentine Sangiovese 1999	*Cherry-strawberry nose, heaps of concentration and satisfying nutty finish – good substitute for overpriced Chianti*
£4.99	9	Argento Malbec 2000	*Dark, dense and liquorous wine by excellent Nicolas Catena – needs food*
£4.99	9	Bright Bros San Juan Reserve Cabernet Sauvignon 1999	*Attractive blackcurrant-and-vanilla wine has robust appeal*
£6.99	10	Bright Brothers Barrica Shiraz 1999	*Top-of-the-range dark, dense and silky vanilla-toned monster (14% alcohol) has sweet lushness but nicely trimmed dry finish*

BULGARIA

| £4.49 | 8 | Boyar Premium Merlot 2000 | *Aside from the horrible lilac-coloured plastic 'cork' this wine isn't bad – middleweight cherry-style* |

Somerfield supermarkets has one of the best ranges of bargain-priced own-label wines – this robust Rhône red costs just £2.99.

FRANCE

£2.99 10 Somerfield Vin de Pays des Coteaux de l'Ardèche 1999
Underpriced bright-fruit ripe southern red with spice and crunch

£3.29 9 Somerfield Côtes de Roussillon 1998
Delicious dark and peppery wine at a great price – the 1999 to follow (tasted under another supermarket's imprimatur) is equally good

£3.49 9 Somerfield Minervois 1998
Warm but not cooked ripe red, surely soon to be superseded by 1999 – not tasted but worth chancing

£3.99 9 Fitou Rocher d'Ambrée 1998
Firm but friendly roasted fruit with soft centre

£4.99 9 Buzet Cuvée 44 1998
I keep coming across this brand, and keep liking it – warm and ripe with peppery hint

ITALY

£2.99 9 Somerfield Sicilian Red 1998
Good-value warm spicy lightweight

£3.99 9 Terrale Primitivo di Puglia 1998
Chewy dark-fruit southern red has nice tarry centre

£4.29 9 Montepulciano d'Abruzzo 1999
Brambly, almost fizzingly lively glugger from Aegean Italy has dense colour and refreshing properties - good cool

£4.49 8 Sangiovese di Maremma 1998
Cherry-scented Chianti substitute has a crisp finish

£4.49 9 Somerfield Cabernet Sauvignon delle Venezia 1999
A perennial favourite, this unusual Italian Cabernet, pleasing abrasion over good cassis fruit

£4.99 8 Terrale Sangiovese 1999
Bright and easy wine has cheery summery fruit and clean finish

SOUTH AFRICA

£7.99 9 Spice Route Pinotage 1999

Exceptionally good burst-of-fruit wine with distinctive acidity – shade pricy

SPAIN

£6.99 9 Viña Cana Rioja Reserva 1995

Relishable creamy mature Rioja has good weight and satisfying strawberry fruit

Among the many well-known brands at Somerfield, this warm, ripe and peppery Gascon red, costing £4.99, stands out.

WHITE WINES

ARGENTINA

| £4.29 | 8 | Somerfield Argentine Chardonnay 2000 | *Medium-built ripe wine with obvious but not inelegant charm* |

AUSTRALIA

| £4.99 | 9 | Pendulum Chardonnay 2000 | *'Concept' wine in a weird silvered bottle looks a lot better in the glass – generous gold colour and good weight in the mouth* |

BULGARIA

| £4.49 | 8 | Boyar Premium Oak Barrel Fermented Chardonnay 2000 | *Pale middleweight has less-overt oak than expected – not bad at the price* |

FRANCE

£3.99	9/10	Domaine du Bois Viognier, Maurel Vedeau, 1999	*Winner on price, this Vin de Pays d'Oc has good peach-and-melon style*
£3.99	9	Les Marionettes Marsanne 1999	*Generous sappy fruit but dry, clean style to this interesting oddity*
£4.99	8	Domaine St Agathe Chardonnay 1998	*Noticeable concentration in this Languedoc coconut-oak wine*
£4.99	8	James Herrick Chardonnay 1999	*Australian-owned Languedoc is most un-Australian in character – pale, crisp and pleasantly vegetal oak-free style*
£5.99	8	Gewürztraminer Caves de Turckheim 1999	*Banker Alsace Gewürz balances sweetness and acidity well*
£6.99	9	Chablis, La Chablisienne, 1999	*Crisp but complex wine with classic stony freshness and plenty of depth*

GREECE

| £3.09 | 9 | Samos Muscat 37.5cl | *A bargain 'dessert' wine golden in colour, honeyed and grape-essence fruit and 15% alcohol* |

ITALY

£2.99	8	Somerfield Sicilian White	*Simple but clean dry white with a whiff of herbs*
£4.29	9	Marc Xero Chardonnay	*Creamy-fruit dry style comes in a frosted bottle*
£4.49	8	Somerfield Chardonnay delle Venzie 1999	*Nice straightforward appley wine from Verona has a creamy note*
£4.49	9/10	Trulli Chardonnay del Salento 1999	*Truly delicious pineapple-perfumed bright rich dry white at a good price*

SOUTH AFRICA

£4.29	8	Kumala Colombard Sauvignon 2000	*Easy mix of melon-tropical fruit and fresh flavours*

PERSONAL NOTES:

. . . .

. . . .

. . . .

. . . .

. . . .

. . . .

. . . .

. . . .

. . . .

. . . .

. . . .

. . . .

. . . .

. . . .

. . . .

TESCO

Britain's biggest retailer reached a new landmark in 2001 by announcing annual profits in excess of £1 billion. It's the first time any supermarket chain has passed this point, and this is surely a sign of the growing dominance of these huge companies.

And yet, I don't worry greatly about Tesco's front place as a retailer of wine, because it offers not just a very large range, but a genuinely interesting one. It has many genuinely good own-label brands (about 20 of them are recommended here), plenty of choice and prices no higher than anywhere else. Like all the other supermarkets, there are regular promotions, modest discounts if you buy a few bottles at a time (5 per cent off any purchase of six or more, including half-bottles) and the usual microscopic savings on the loyalty card.

I have to say I would not make a special journey to a Tesco solely for the purpose of buying wine. But then the point of buying wine in supermarkets is that you are already there intent on buying a great deal of other merchandise. And as such, Tesco is fine.

The range is particularly strong on the New World, with a more inspired Australian collection, including many good own-labels, than any of the other supermarkets. But don't ignore the French and Italian wines, which continue a long tradition here of well-sought-out brands.

Because it is such a vast network of stores – 566 at the last count – ranging from relatively dinky Metro outlets to hypermarkets bigger than football pitches, the extent of the wine range carried does vary from branch to branch. This does mean you cannot count on finding all of the wines mentioned here in every branch. But you can if you wish check whether your local store carries any particular wine by ringing the freecall central Customer Service line on 0800 505555.

Tesco also happens to have one of the best-designed websites, at www.tesco.com. It features regularly changing offers of mixed cases, at prices reduced by as much as a third from what you would pay in store. Online shoppers should take note, but so should any wine enthusiast planning a visit to a store, because the special offers online are quite separate from those promoted in the supermarkets themselves.

ARGENTINA

£4.99 4 Deep Purple Shiraz 2000

Iffy nail-polish nose on the sample I tasted, and it wasn't even notably purple – unless you count the colour of the gimmicky bottle

£4.99 9/10 Santa Julia Oak-aged Merlot 2000

Keen-edged fruit on this lively young red

£5.99 9/10 Santa Julia Bonarda/Sangiovese Reserva 1999

Minty nose and fruit and the cherry brightness of the Italian grape varieties make this balanced wine particularly relishable

AUSTRALIA

£3.99 8 Angove's Lock 9 Carignan/ Mataro/Shiraz 2000

Curious, woody-spirity sort of wine that might suit rugged thirsts

£3.99 9 Casella Carramar Estate Merlot 2000

Juicy soft young red that will chill well – cheap by Oz standards

£4.99 9 Angove's Stonegate Barbera 2000

Dark opaque Italian-style wine has more plumpness than the original might, and a curious caramel note – enjoyable

£5.99 11 Miranda Rovalley Ridge Petit Verdot 2000

Bright purply colour and a gorgeous creamy-smoky nose give way to finely balanced fruit in this hearty but elegant wine, which finishes with a delicious bite

£5.99 7 Tesco's Finest McLaren Vale Grenache 1999

Pale, jam-nosed, soft-fruit crowd-pleaser

£6.99 9 Tesco Finest Coonawarra Cabernet Sauvignon 1997

Deep colour is turning brown with age in this glyceriney, mouth-gripping and minty – and rather subtly delicious – Bordeaux-style Oz red

£6.99	9	Tesco Finest McLaren Vale Shiraz 1999	*Huge, squishy, yielding mouthful of ripe plummy fruit in this generous (14% alcohol) deep-purple smoothie*
£8.99	9	Brown Bros Graciano 1997	*Densely coloured, weighty (13.5% alcohol) stuff with a eucalyptus nose and scrummy spicy fruit – most interesting and un-Australian, it should evolve for years*
£8.99	9	Wilkie Estate Organic Cabernet Merlot 2000	*So dark it's near-enough black, this Adelaide slurper has a pleasing steeped-grapeskin nose and robust summer-pudding fruit – immediately appealing and justifies the price*

CHILE

£4.99	9/10	Tesco Chilean Merlot Reserve 2000	*Bright berry top edge on the nose of this meaty (13.5% alcohol) red with a dark, liquorice heart amidst juicy-ripe fruit*
£4.99	9	Tesco Finest Chilean Cabernet Sauvignon Reserve 2000	*Soft, 'upfront' fruit is somehow typically Chilean – a satisfying ripe blackcurrant-and-vanilla formula with 13.5% alcohol*
£7.99	10	Vision Merlot Reserve 2000	*Very dense dark colour and a generous morello nose suggesting the rich, cushiony fruit beyond, this is terrific – note 14% alcohol*

FRANCE

£3.99	8	Neptune Carignan 2000	*A vin de pays from Luberon in Provence, this is a bright young thing: a gluggable spiceburger with relishable sunny grip – the odd name comes from flying winemaker Peter Harvey, ex-Australian Air Force Neptune jet pilot*

£3.99	10	Tesco Finest Corbières Reserve La Sansoure 2000	*Purple-black, jammy-nosed slurper by excellent Mont Tauch co-op in Languedoc is thrillingly mellow and juicy – and cheap*
£4.99	10	Le Monstre Grenache Noir 2000	*Name's a bit of a turn-off, but this soupy, leathery, coffee-toned Languedoc giant (it has 14% alcohol) is ripe and relishable*
£4.99	9	Tesco Finest Côtes du Rhône Villages Reserve 2000	*Spearmint and spice on nose of a gripping young wine that will surely drink at its best from 2002, or later*
£4.99	8	Tesco Finest Fitou Baron de la Tour Reserve 1999	*Well-balanced, slightly tough middleweight for barbecue occasions*
£5.99	10	Calvet Reserve 1998	*Brilliant Bordeaux brand has wet-cellar-floor nose with cassis bubbling up from below – a balanced middleweight claret of unaccustomed quality in this price range*
£6.99	4	Juliénas Georges Duboeuf 1999	*Raw, rubbery Beaujolais cru that doesn't live up to the lyrical label*
£7.99	8	Perrin Vacqueyras 1998	*Spicy-nosed, tannin-laden Rhône village wine is good but pricy*

GERMANY

| £3.99 | 8 | Fire Mountain Pinot Noir 1999 | *Pale bricky colour and ethereal nose on this unusual Rheinpfalz red, but nice crisp raspberry fruit – earthy and slight, but enjoyable* |

HUNGARY

| £3.99 | 8 | Riverview Kekfrankos/Merlot 2000 | *Stalky nose and leafy fruit in a wine with clean directness – not bad at the price* |

ITALY

£4.99 9/10 Inycon Merlot 1999

Nice spearmint waft off this handsomely coloured Sicilian wine with dark, peppery fruit – gripping stuff and 14.5% alcohol

£4.99 10/11 Inycon Syrah 2000

Dense and dark to the point of opacity, this huge (14.5% alcohol) Sicilian has massive briary fruit with a roasty, liquorice heart – terrific value

NEW ZEALAND

£5.99 9/10 Babich Cabernet Franc/Pinotage 1999

Strange mix of South African and Bordeaux grapes makes for a raspberry-toned middleweight with the character of Burgundy!

£6.99 8 Montana Pinotage 2000

Classic Pinotage has brambles and cream and resembles indigenous South African style

USA

£5.99 9 Tesco Finest West California Zinfandel Reserve 1999

Bright and healthy wine with warm, sunny fruit is lush and likeable

AUSTRALIA

£4.99 9/10 Mount Hurtle Grenache Rosé 2000

Screwtop-bottled pink has pale magenta colour, generous blackberry nose and soft summer fruit with maximum freshness

CHILE

£4.49 8 Valdivieso Malbec Rosé 2000

Very pale pink and a caramel whiff, but it's a fresh and gutsy dry style of wine of more interest than most rosé

FRANCE

£3.99 9 Tesco Côtes du Rhône Rosé 2000

Very pale colour indeed but actually quite positively fruity in a cherryish sort of way. Clean and brisk – and cheap

£4.49 8 Celsius Cabernet Sauvignon Rosé 2000

Vin de Pays d'Oc with plenty of colour and a keen attack (first flavour sensation in the mouth) of summer fruits with a crisp finish

SOUTH AFRICA

£4.99 9 Goats do Roam Rosé 2000

Very pale salmon colour with soft but refreshing strawberry fruit – ripe (13.5% alcohol) and satisfying

USA

£5.99 9/10 Fetzer Syrah Rosé 2000

Exciting summer-pudding nose followed by matching fruit; quite delicious, very easy drinking

ARGENTINA

£3.99 6 La Nature Organic Torrontes 2000 *Peppery Muscat nose is typical of the Torrontes grape but this dry white is a bit hard edged*

£5.99 9 Candela Viognier 2000 *Likeable freshness to this well-proportioned off-dry tropical-fruit softie*

AUSTRALIA

£4.99 7 ICE2 Medium Chardonnay 2000 *From excellent Miranda Wines in SE Australia, this strange mélange does taste of Chardonnay and does, too, have a honey hint from the small proportion of 'noble rot' late-harvest grapes – a concocted wine for the sweet-toothed, presumably*

£5.99 10 Tesco Finest Great Southern Riesling 2000 *Very pale colour but a marvellously contrived lush-limey dry white of real interest that will repay keeping*

£5.99 8 Tesco Finest Hunter Valley Semillon 2000 *Tesco say this wine will age gracefully, but for now it is a simple fresh, crisp young dry white with the faintest honey-hint of the Semillon grape*

£5.99 9 Tesco Finest Padthaway Chardonnay 2000 *An eager wine artfully matching oaked richness with freshness – try it with roast chicken*

£6.99 9 Wilkie Estate Organic Verdelho 2000 *Well-coloured dryish white with pleasant canned-pineapple nose and butterscotch heart to the fruit – rather lush*

CHILE

£4.99 10 Isla Negra Chardonnay 2000

An extravagant wine with real wraparound rich flavours, this scores especially high for exuberant freshness; Isla Negra is a brand of the leading Casablanca producer Viña Cono Sur

£4.99 9 Tesco Finest Chilean Chardonnay Reserve 2000

Made by Chile's best known producer Valdivieso, a weighty wine, but so crisp it prickles the mouth at the finish

FRANCE

£2.99 8 Tesco Simply Sauvignon 2000

Vin de Pays d'Oc has an emphatically sea-grass Sauvignon nose and eager fruit – the grapefruit element stops just short of sour

£3.99 7 Château Talmont 2000

A soft-centred, low-acidity retreating dry white from the classic Sauvignon-Semillon grape blend of Bordeaux's Entre Deux Mers region

£4.49 8 Celsius Medium Chardonnay 2000

Quite a sweet Vin de Pays d'Oc and better than Liebfraumilch – from which it is presumably intended as a refuge

£4.99 6 Kiwi Cuvée Sauvignon Blanc 2000

An attempt at vin de pays level in the Loire Valley at replicating the zing and zap of New Zealand Sauvignon is only moderately successful

£5.99 8 Tesco Finest Alsace Gewürztraminer 1999

Nose positively billows with lychee aroma from this rather sweet wine by an individual grower, Rene Kuehn, rather than the usual cooperative source favoured by supermarkets

£6.99 7 Tesco Finest Chablis 2000

A nice light wine but not really expressive of the true Chablis style

£6.99 9 Tesco Finest Sancerre 2000

*Brisk and breezy example of this
popular Loire-appellation Sauvignon
at an unusually reasonable price*

GERMANY

£6.99 10/11 Bernkasteler Graben Riesling
Kabinett 1999

*Generous, grapy, racy young Mosel
Riesling in the lush but minerally-
fresh sweet-apple style – a great
aperitif wine, and only 8.5% alcohol*

HUNGARY

£3.99 8 Riverview Chardonnay/
Pinot Grigio 2000

*Colour looks pink-tinged and there's
plenty of mildly spicy fruit in the
curious mélange*

ITALY

£4.99 6 Lamberti Pinot Grigio 2000

*Fresh floral nose on this big-brand
promises much, but the wine is
ordinary*

£4.99 10/11 Inycon Chardonnay 2000

*OK, it's a popular brand – just about
all the supermarkets now have it –
but this Sicilian masterpiece by the
huge Settesoli co-operative is just
great: gold colour, fresh, appley
classic chardonnay nose (no oak
involved), heaps of ripeness (14%
alcohol) and flavours sublimely
orchestrated into a beginning, a
middle and an end*

NEW ZEALAND

£4.99 9 Nobilo White Cloud 1999

*This old-fashioned wine in the
medium, grapy Germanic style that
once typified Kiwi whites has been
getting more sophisticated in recent
vintages – an easy, fresh glassful at a
good price*

£5.99	9	Montana Unoaked Chardonnay 2000	*Appetising pure-fruit shardy from NZ's biggest winery has zest and concentration*
£6.49	9	Tesco Finest Marlborough Sauvignon Blanc 2000	*There's asparagus at the bottom of this greengrocery basket making for an intriguing, relatively low-acidity wine*

PERSONAL NOTES:

. . . .

. . . .

. . . .

. . . .

. . . .

. . . .

. . . .

Tesco brims with New World bargains but don't overlook the excellent range of French 'country' wines such as this purple-black, jammy-nosed red at £3.99.

THRESHER, WINE RACK AND BOTTOMS UP – AND VICTORIA WINE

These shops are the surviving 'brands' of Britain's biggest high-street off-licence chain, First Quench – the 3,000-branch conglomerate formed in 1999 by the union of Thresher with Victoria Wine. Taken over in 2000 by Japanese bank Nomura, the decision has been taken by the new management to kill off the Victoria Wine branches and 're-brand' them as Thresher shops (except, interestingly, in Scotland where Victoria Wine has a loyal following). Many of the shops will simply shut down. Thus ends the 136-year history of Britain's first – and largest – wine-merchant chain.

It's a sign of the times. Until the 1970s, traditional off-licences had the take-home wine and spirit market almost entirely to themselves. Now, shops of this type account for less than a fifth of off-licence sales, and I cannot see how this share can do anything other than shrink further.

As wine becomes more of an everyday grocery item in so many households, so has it looked more at home in the supermarket trolley. It makes a visit to a dedicated wine merchant as needless a diversion from the weekly supermarket blitz as to any of the other high-street grocers, butchers, bakers and fishmongers who have been so ruthlessly exterminated by the multiples.

If the likes of Thresher really wish to compete, they will surely have to offer something the supermarkets don't – namely skilled service, wines unique to themselves (including positive own brands) and truly competitive prices. But in none of these respects has Thresher improved during the brief tenures of its last two managements. True, the biggest disadvantage for high-street retailers is probably their inability to offer car parking and Thresher will never be able to do anything about that, but even the company's attempt at online wine retailing, branded 'enjoyment.co.uk', failed within one year.

What next? The company is now run by David Williams, who made his name at Burger King, and has announced that First Quench 'has a marvellous opportunity to consolidate its leadership of the specialist off-licence market'.

RED WINES

ARGENTINA

£3.99 9/10 Corazon Bonarda 2000 — *Darkly delicious sleek red has satisfying ripeness*

£4.99 9 Argento Malbec 2000 — *Dark, dense and liquorous wine by excellent Nicolas Catena – needs food*

£8.99 9/10 Norton Privada 1998 — *Bordeaux grape varieties combine in an opulent oaked cedary classic red*

AUSTRALIA

£4.99 9 Lindemans Cawarra Shiraz Cabernet 2000 — *Decent spicy wine is light by Oz standards but satisfying*

£6.99 9 Rosemount Shiraz Cabernet 2000 — *Juicy and spicy berry-fruit dark style is relishably brambly*

£9.99 9/10 Tim Adams The Fergus 1998 — *Sumptuously oaky and soft Grenache with a 'mulberry' character – wine for a special occasion*

CHILE

£5.99 9 Santa Ines Carmenère Reserve 1999 — *Slinky blackberry-fruit ripe wine*

£7.99 8 Errazuriz Reserve Cabernet Sauvignon 1998 — *Rather dense and still-tannic wine with lots of cassis fruit – needs time*

£8.99 7 Valdivieso Single Vineyard Cabernet Franc 1998 — *Likeable oak-enhanced dark wine seems rather expensive*

FRANCE

£4.99 9 Chasse Du Pape Reserve 1998 — *Benefits from time in bottle, a solid, spicy Côtes du Rhône*

£5.99 10 Calvet Reserve 1998 — *Brilliant Bordeaux brand has wet-cellar-floor nose with cassis bubbling up from below – a balanced middleweight claret of unaccustomed quality in this price range*

£5.99	9	L'Excellence de Capendu 1998	*I'm a dedicated follower of this top producer in the Corbières AC – this is their oak-smooth 'reserve' wine*
£6.49	9/10	Valréas, Domaine Grande Bellane, Côtes du Rhône Villages 1999	*Superb peppery-briary dark concentrated wine with a long future but cheaper elsewhere*
£8.99	9/10	Louis Jadot Pinot Noir 1998	*Lovely strawberry-nosed village Burgundy is authentically ripe and earthy*

ITALY

| £6.99 | 9 | Formulae, Barone Ricasoli, 1998 | *Interesting non-DOCG Chianti made by the family who 'invented' Chianti 150 years ago – hefty fruit and clean finish* |

NEW ZEALAND

| £8.99 | 9/10 | Church Road Cabernet Sauvignon/Merlot | *Arrestingly delicious silky Bordeaux-style wine with the characteristic minty vigour of NZ reds* |
| £9.99 | 9/10 | Montana Reserve Pinot Noir 1999 | *Marvellous rich eucalyptus-and-red-berry wine of great concentration (and 14% alcohol) has unique style* |

PORTUGAL

£3.79	9	Ramada 1999	*Interesting minty red suggests cloves and honey amidst the dark fruit – and the 2000 vintage is equally good*
£3.99	9	Terra Boa 1999	*Sweet nose but keenly edged dark fruit to this workmanlike red from Tras-Os-Montes region*
£4.99	9	Segada Trincadeira Preta-Castelao 1999	*Love this juicy darkly spicy and minty food wine*

SOUTH AFRICA

| £6.99 | 9 | Delheim Pinotage 1998 | *Nice marriage of vigorous juiciness and ripe concentration* |

SPAIN

£4.49 8 Viña Albali Tinto Reserva 1995 *Emphatically vanilla-oaked mature Valdepeñas is light-ish but satisfying*

£4.99 9/10 Viña del Recuerdo 1997 *Worth making the journey for this oaky Navarra with lush blackcurrant depths*

USA

£6.49 9 Redwood Trail Pinot Noir 1998 *Perennial favourite from California is brimming with sunny strawberry-raspberry aromas and flavours*

£6.99 9 Fetzer Valley Oaks Cabernet Sauvignon 1998 *Rich, spirity nose gives way to a gently ripe and deliciously squishy easy-drinking wine*

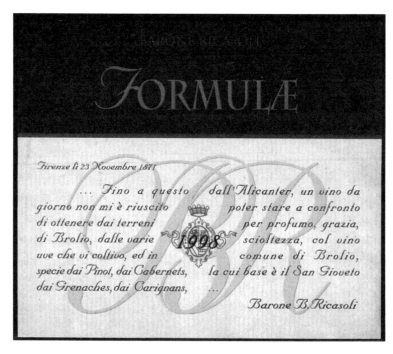

Thresher is replacing interesting individual wines with more 'gobal brands' but an exception is this hefty and interesting red from chianti country at £6.99.

ARGENTINA
£4.49 8 Norton Torrontes 2000 *Agreeable table-grape-scented soft dry white*

AUSTRALIA
£4.49 9 Lindemans Cawarra Unoaked Chardonnay 2000 *Cleverly contrived big brand has purity and creaminess and impressive citrus finish*

CHILE
£4.99 9/10 Isla Negra Chardonnay 2000 *An extravagant wine with real wraparound rich flavours, this scores especially high for exuberant freshness; Isla Negra is a brand of the leading Casablanca producer Viña Cono Sur*

FRANCE
£3.99 8 Alsace Blanc 1999 *Fresh herbaceous dry white with a whiff of the exotic*

£4.99 9 French Revolution 1999 *From the Loire, a successful mix of soft Chenin Blanc and crisp Sauvignon Blanc – scores for refreshment value as well as interest*

£4.99 9 James Herrick Chardonnay 1999 *Australian-owned Vin de Pays d'Oc has dependable mineral character*

£4.99 6 Kiwi Cuvée Sauvignon Blanc 2000 *An attempt at vin de pays level in the Loire Valley at replicating the zing and zap of New Zealand Sauvignon is only moderately successful*

£5.99 7 Fat Bastard Chardonnay 1999 *Ordinary oaky Vin de Pays d'Oc that has spawned a whole genre of dismal brands with even worse names*

£5.99 9 Tokay Pinot Gris, Cave de Turckheim, 1998 *Exotic middleweight from Alsace has smoky-spicy flavours*

GERMANY

£5.99 9 Kendermann Cellar Selection *Dry Moselle has ripe grapy depths*
Riesling Spätlese 1999 *and racy fruit*

ITALY

£4.99 9 Marc Xero Chardonnay *Creamy-fruit dry style comes in a*
frosted bottle

NEW ZEALAND

£6.99 9 Oyster Bay Marlborough *Happy mix of flinty freshness and*
Chardonnay 2000 *sweet-apple lusciousness*

£7.99 9 Montana Reserve Barrique *Golden-coloured and opulently*
Fermented Chardonnay 1999 *flavoured old-fashioned rich but*
balanced wine

£8.99 8 Craggy Range Sauvignon Blanc *Ripe style (and 13.7% alcohol) with a*
2000 *distinct brassica nose – pleasing but*
untypical

£9.99 9 Villa Maria Sauvignon Blanc *Lashings of gooseberry fruit and a*
Reserve 2000 *certain profundity in this top-flight*
Marlborough wine – nice hint of
residual sweetness

SPAIN

£5.49 9 Viña Esmeralda, Miquel Torres, *Weirdly wonderful spicy-aromatic dry*
1999 *white has unique character*

USA

£7.99 8 Fetzer Viognier 1999 *Peachy example of this popular genre*
is delicious but pricier than some
rivals

£8.49 10 Bonterra Chardonnay 1999 *A personal favourite, this organic*
Californian has extraordinary purity

VICTORIA WINE

See Thresher

WAITROSE

Let's be perfectly straightforward about this. Waitrose is, by a mile, is the best supermarket from which to buy wine. True, the chain has one obvious shortcoming – that its branches are concentrated in the southern reaches of England, but determined followers of their wines can buy all of them (and a good many not even stocked in the shops) from the firm's now well-established mail-order service, Waitrose Wine Direct.

So what's so good about Waitrose? I believe it's that they just seem to have the best of everything. Instead of filling the shelves with big brands from Australia and California, they offer the best choice of French country and classic-region wines of any supermarket, the best German range of any supermarket and the most interesting collection of wines from Italy and Spain. They have only a small number of own-brand wines, but what there is, is good.

Waitrose stores enjoy (I'm sure the word 'enjoy' is right) a reputation for being 'posh' – and thus for being expensive. Well, while I cannot speak for the fresh fruit or cornflake sections, I can certainly state with confidence that Waitrose wines are no more expensive than wines from any other supermarket. And Waitrose has now started offering quite-generous discounts on a couple of dozen different wines every month – something I have never seen them do before.

In short, while other supermarkets stand still, Waitrose seems to be moving forward.

Waitrose Wine Direct, Freepost (SW 1647), Bracknell RG12 8HX. Tel 0800 188881. Website www.waitrose.com.

RED WINES

ARGENTINA

£4.49 9/10 Santa Julia Bonarda-
                Sangiovese 2000

Cherries and blackberries in this structured, lush middleweight – very easy drinking indeed

£6.99 9 Balbi Malbec Reserva 1999

Mouthgripping purply-black vanilla-toned wine has agreeable tannin and will certainly repay keeping for several years

AUSTRALIA

£4.99 9 Fisherman's Bend Cabernet
              Sauvignon 1999

Over-the-top extra-ripe slurper has extravagant 'upfront' fruit, but modest 13% alcohol, and lots of easy charm – barbecue wine

£7.99 9/10 Garry Crittenden Barbera 'i' 1999

Bouncy blackberry fruit in a smooth, sleek texture, this is in the grand Italian style – quite delicious

CHILE

£4.49 7 Concha y Toro Merlot 2000

Famous producer, but rather a stringy wine

£5.99 10 Mont Gras Carmenère Reserva
               2000

Top-class intensely concentrated berry-ripe red has silky mouthfeel

£6.49 9 Errazuriz Cabernet Sauvignon
              1999

Gripping muscular red has 13.5% alcohol and concentrated cassis fruit – should just be at peak maturity in 2002

£8.99 7 Valdivieso Single Vineyard
              Cabernet Franc 1998

Likeable oak-enhanced dark wine seems rather expensive

FRANCE

£3.49 7 Vin de Pays d'Aigues Merlot-
              Cabernet Sauvignon 2000

Distinctly brambly young style

£3.59	9	Waitrose Côtes du Rhône 2000	*Rather pale and raw colour, but this fresh and sunny ripe young red (13.5% alcohol) is very easy to drink, and good value*
£3.79	9	Côtes du Ventoux 2000	*Brambly, well-constructed Rhône red with 13.5% alcohol*
£3.99	7	Bistro Rouge 2000	*'Suitable for vegetarians and vegans' but rather a hard Vin de Pays d'Oc*
£3.99	7	Fortant Grenache Vin de Pays d'Oc 2000	*All-purpose sweet-woody big brand of so-so quality*
£3.99	8	Maury Vin Doux Naturel	*Raisiny mildly fortified (16.5% alcohol) ultra-sweet wine to sip chilled with puddings – or blue cheese*
£3.99	8	Waitrose Good Ordinary Claret	*Decent, not-too-green red Bordeaux worthy of the name*
£4.99	8	Abbotts Ammonite Côtes du Roussillon 1999	*Briary nose and soft but solid fruit*
£4.99	8	Waitrose Special Reserve Claret 1999	*The nose is the best bit – a thoroughly authentic blackberry-and-cedar whiff – and the fruit is tannic but* souple, *as the French say*
£5.49	9	Château Haut d'Allard, Côtes de Bourg, 1998	*Ready-to-drink claret has ripe roundness and evident concentration – stands out*
£5.49	9	Ermitage du Pic Saint Loup 1999	*Leafy nose on a big (13.5% alcohol) coffee-edged solid Languedoc red*
£5.99	9	Château Pech-Latt 1999	*Good-hearted organic Corbières is robust and ripe*
£6.49	9	La Cuvée Mythique 1998	*Upmarket Vin de Pays d'Oc has spice and grip amidst dense smoothness – fleshy but nicely edged*
£6.99	9	Saint Chinian, Château Cazal-Viel Cuvée des Fées, 1999	*Dark, liquorice-bottomed Midi red promises delicious drinking in future – one to keep two or three years*

£6.99	9	Château de Targe, Saumur Champigny, 1999	*Classic Loire red has attractive leafiness over sunny, cassis fruit*
£6.99	9	Corbières, Château de Caraguilhes, 1998	*Tarry centre to this sweet and spicy maturing oaked red with a lipsmacking finish*
£9.95	9	Savigny-lès-Beaune, Caves des Hautes Côtes, 1999	*Decent co-operative Burgundy has warm and welcoming soft fruit charm – classic earthy Pinot Noir for now or to keep*
£9.99	10	Château Beauchêne Châteauneuf du Pape 1999	*Lovely complex smell on this richly endowed classic red which is already delicious to drink in spite of its youth – easily the best supermarket Châteauneuf I've found and of rare quality within a £10 budget*
£9.99	8	Château des Jacques, Moulin-à-Vent 1999	*Good-quality Beaujolais cru from dependable négociant Louis Jadot will be just right for dinking in 2002*

GREECE

£3.89	9	Pathos Xinamavro, Tsantali, 1999	*Lively red has bright colour and keen edgy fruit – surprisingly good*

ITALY

£3.99	9	Buonasera, Argiolas	*'Good evening' wine from Sardinia has a sweet, rustic style with a whiff of the maquis – works well*
£3.99	7	Il Padrino Sangiovese 2000	*Stark purple wine from Sicily, is rather sweet*
£3.99	8	Nero d'Avola/Syrah, Firriato, 2000	*Cherry nose, earthy style from Sicily*
£3.99	9/10	Waitrose Chianti 1999	*Made by ubiquitous firm of Cecchi this does taste like Chianti – brisk cherry fruit, nutskin finish – and as such is very good value*

£4.99	9/10	Albera Barbera d'Asti Superiore 1999	*Nice bitter finish on this perky but sleekly fruity Piedmont – loads of character*
£4.99	8	Terra Viva Merlot del Veneto 2000	*Organic red looks a bit raw and has a woody-stalky style but does have clean-dry fruit that will go well with food*
£4.99	9	Vigna Alta Merlot/Cabernet, Venosa, 2000	*Dense purply-looking stuff takes a firm grip on the tastebuds – quality food wine*
£7.49	9/10	Chianti Classico, Rocca di Castagnoli, 1998	*Extravagant oak-aged wine has a roasty, opulent style but still has the delicious brambly vigour of the best Chianti*

MEXICO

| £4.99 | 9 | LA Cetto Petite Sirah 1998 | *Dark, young-looking minty red* |

NEW ZEALAND

| £9.99 | 9/10 | Montana Reserve Pinot Noir 1999 | *Marvellous rich eucalyptus-and-red-berry wine of great concentration (and 14% alcohol) has unique style* |

PORTUGAL

£4.99	9	Vinha do Monte 1999	*Typical sappy, keen-edged Portuguese style from unpronounceable indigenous grapes grown in Alentejo region*
£5.49	9	Altano, Symington, 1999	*From the Douro valley, home of port, this dark-purple brew is distinctly reminiscent of the fortified wine, but gently delicious and not overstrong at 12% alcohol*
£5.99	8	Manta Preta 1999	*Very dry first flavour gives way to agreeable glyceriney dark fruit*
£7.49	8	Trincadeira, JP Ramos, 1999	*Mild-mannered vanilla-oaky midweight*

| £7.99 | 9/10 | Vila Santa, JP Ramos, 1999 | *Luxury red from Alentejo is young and strong (14% alcohol) with chewy, mouth-coating fruit and great charm* |

ROMANIA

| £3.69 | 8 | Willow Ridge Pinot Noir/Merlot, Dealu Mare, 1999 | *Simple earthy red is light in colour but firm in fruit* |

SOUTH AFRICA

| £3.99 | 9 | Culemborg Cape Red 2000 | *Pale-looking, maraschino-nose big brand has good balance and looks very fair value* |

| £4.99 | 9 | Goats do Roam 2000 | *Name is supposed to resemble 'Côtes du Rhône' but principal grape is Cape's native Pinotage – a flavoursome spicy glugger (13.5% alcohol)* |

SPAIN

| £3.49 | 9 | Gran Lopez Tinto, Campo de Borja, 1999 | *Peppery-sweet style to a mature-tasting pale-coloured wine* |

| £3.99 | 7 | Totally Tinto | *Eye-catching label but not an improvement of previous blend* |

| £5.89 | 9/10 | Viña Herminia Rioja Crianza 1996 | *Lovely strawberry-vanilla whiff off this bargain-priced mature Rioja with generous round fruit and grippy tannin* |

USA

| £6.49 | 7 | Ironstone Vineyards Zinfandel 1998 | *Strong (14% alcohol) rather anonymous Californian red* |

| £6.99 | 9 | Fetzer Valley Oaks Cabernet Sauvignon 1998 | *Rich, spirity nose gives way to a gently ripe and deliciously squishy easy-drinking wine* |

| £9.99 | 9/10 | Bonterra Vineyards Merlot 1997 | *Pricy but immensely enjoyable organic Californian has dark, ripe morello-cherry style – luscious mature subtly oaked wine for special occasions* |

PINK WINES

FRANCE

£3.99   7   Winter Hill Syrah Rosé 2000   *Mildly prickly, orange-hued Vin de Pays d'Oc*

HUNGARY

£3.49   8   Nagyrede Cabernet Sauvignon Rosé 2000   *Pale, mild-mannered pink does have some crispness, and is very cheap*

WHITE WINES

ARGENTINA

£4.49   9   Bodega Lurton Pinot Gris 2000   *Proper smoky style to this fascinating Mendoza wine, and it's cheap*

£6.49   9/10   Santa Julia Viognier Reserve 2000   *Spirity nose and 14% alcohol with a likeable caramel centre to this super-ripe oaked wine*

£8.99   10   Catena Agrelo Vineyards Chardonnay 1999   *A personal favourite year after year, this has ideal balance of weight and concentration with minerality and focused fruit*

AUSTRALIA

£3.99   8   Currawong Creek Chardonnay 2000   *Rich colour, sweet nose, appley fruit – decent Chardonnay plonk at a fair price*

£4.99   9   Jindalee Chardonnay 2000   *Lots of sweet-apple fruit for your money*

£6.49   9   Oxford Landing Limited Release Viognier 2000   *Exotic apricot-scented honeyed-but-freshly-dry white offering real interest*

£6.99   10   Charleston Pinot Gris 2000   *Smoky, exotic-fruit classic with wonderfully poised richness-dryness and lots of alcohol (14%)*

£8.99   9/10   Nepenthe Vineyards Riesling 2000   *Jolly brisk acidity on this lush limey and emphatic wine (note 14% alcohol) that leaves a big impression*

£8.99	8	Nepenthe Vineyards Sauvignon Blanc 2000	*A sort of 'luxury' Sauvignon with depth and complexity*
£9.99	8	Cape Mentelle Semillon/ Sauvignon 2000	*Famous Margaret River producer's blend has exotic scent, fleshy fruit and easy briskness but rather a high price-tag*
£9.99	7	Greg Norman Estates Yarra Valley Chardonnay 2000	*Good but unremarkable brand from the winery owned by Australia's famous golfer*
£9.99	9	Yalumba Eden Valley Viognier 1999	*Toast-and-butter style to this rich and plump heavyweight (note 14.5% alcohol) and very likeable even at the price*

AUSTRIA

| £5.99 | 8 | Münzenrieder Beerenauslese 1997 37.5cl | *A very sweet 'dessert' wine with flavours dominated by raisins – delicious if you like that sort of thing* |

CANADA

| £6.99 | 8 | Mission Hill Private Reserve Pinot Blanc 1999 | *Forest-pine whiff to this crisp but fleshy dry white from British Columbia – good but a tad pricy* |

CHILE

£3.99	8	Canepa Semillon 2000	*All-purpose soft-dry white of indeterminate character*
£4.99	8	Caliterra Chardonnay 2000	*Hint of coconutty oak and fleshy-appley fruit*
£4.99	9	35 South Sauvignon Blanc 2000	*Very fresh, almost briny, aroma and crisp, tangy style to this well-priced refresher*
£5.49	9	Carmen Vineyards Gewürztraminer 1999	*Well-coloured, lychee-scented spicy dry wine of character – ideal with oriental food*

FRANCE

£2.99	8	Boulder Creek 2000	*Simple clean dry Vaucluse white offering respectable value*
£3.99	9	La Cité Chardonnay 2000	*Honey-wax smell and wholsesome toffee-toned fruit on this relishable Vin de Pays d'Oc*
£3.99	7	Waitrose Chardonnay 2000	*Edgy, near-austere style for those who like their Chardonnay very dry indeed*
£3.99	9	Waitrose Touraine Sauvignon Blanc 2000	*Pebbly nose, lightweight lemon-finishing bargain refresher from the Loire*
£4.79	9	Picpoul de Pinet, Château de Petit Roubié, 2000	*Zesty, almost briny, style to this floral-scented Rhône curio – organically made and easy to drink*
£4.99	9	La Baume Viognier 2000	*Typical apricot nose and lingering slinky fruit in this ripe (14% alcohol) Vin de Pays d'Oc*
£4.99	8	Mâcon-Villages Chardonnay, Cave de Lugny, 2000	*Spearmint whiff on a keen lightweight southern Burgundy*
£4.99	9	Muscat de Beaumes-de-Venise	*Mildly fortified ultra-sweet wine that tastes as if the pips have been incorporated into the flavour – fun and cheap, to be served very well chilled*
£5.99	8	Château Thieuley 2000	*Well-known Bordeaux estate's dry white has a raddishy middle fruit – very crisp and clean*
£5.99	9/10	Waitrose Alsace Gewürztraminer 1999	*High mark for this because it's fresher with less residual sugar than most current supermarket Gewürzes – but the producer is not named on the label*

£7.59	10	Château Carsin Cuvée Prestige 1998	*Honey-pineapple nose like a rich Sauternes, but this is a dry Bordeaux, with brilliant balance of lushness and freshness – exciting wine*
£8.49	7	Pouilly Fumé, Chatelain, 1999	*Fine Loire wine has alluring almondy smell and keen Sauvignon fruit but seems a shade pricy*
£8.99	9/10	Château Vignal Labrie, Monbazillac, 1997	*This honeyed 'dessert' wine has a gorgeous rich colour, an exciting perfume and flavour, and excellent clean finish – deserves attention in a realm where good examples under a tenner are rare*
£9.99	9	Fortant 'F' Limited Release Chardonnay 1998	*Top wine from famed Fortant range of vins de pays has fine gold colour, opulent smell and handsome, minerally fruit*

GERMANY

£3.99	8	Hedgerow 2000 Rheinhessen	*Silly name for an OK and very dry, brisk 'modern' German wine*
£4.99	9/10	Bernkasteler-Kueser Weisenstein Riesling Spätlese 1998	*Distinct honey-and-diesel style and flavours in depth – excellent Moselle at this price*
£6.49	9	Riesling, Bassermann Jordan, 2000	*Straightforward, even elegant, grapey, appley balanced sleek hock*
£6.99	9/10	Erdener Treppchen Riesling Spätlese, Stefar Ehlan, 1997	*Sweet-apple nose and lush, ripe, soft fruit with a hint of flint on the finish make this Moselle very yummy indeed*
£7.99	8	Bernkasteler Badstübe Riesling Spätlese, Dr Thanisch, 1997	*Softly appealing Moselle is delicious but doesn't match other Waitrose German wines for value*

HUNGARY

£2.99	9/10	Matra Springs 2000	*Exotic Muscat nose, soft herbaceous fruit – good value for a delicious aperitif wine*
£4.29	9	Deer Leap Sauvignon Blanc 2000	*Nettles! – crisp and fresh, and the price won't sting you*

ITALY

£3.99	8	Buongiorno Argiolas	*Light, eggy dry white from Sardinia*
£3.99	7	Mezzomondo Chardonnay, Valgarina, 2000	*Wildly oaky dry white with pleasant but retreating fruit*
£3.99	9	Zagara Catarratto Chardonnay Firriato 2000	*Lots of colour in this Sicilian with mint and toffee on nose and in fruit – formulaic but friendly*
£4.29	8	Orvieto Classico Secco, Cardeto, 2000	*Has characteristic blossomy nose and a soft acidity*
£4.79	9	Verdicchio dei Castelli di Jesi Classico, Moncaro, 2000	*Creamy texture in this organic dry herbaceous wine with good persistence of flavour*
£4.85	8	Sauvignon Friuli, San Simone, 2000	*Generous whiff of grassy Sauvignon and plenty of fruit*
£4.99	10/11	Inycon Chardonnay 2000	*OK, it's a popular brand – just about all the supermarkets now have it – but this Sicilian masterpiece by the huge Settesoli co-operative is just great: gold colour, fresh, appley classic Chardonnay nose (no oak involved), heaps of ripeness (14% alcohol) and flavours sublimely orchestrated into a beginning, a middle and an end*
£4.99	9	Soave Classico Vigneto Colombara, Zenato, 2000	*Crisp, bright and pure example of a famous but often disappointing name – this is good by any standard*

| £5.99 | 8 | Pinot Grigio Alto Adige, San Michele-Appiano, 2000 | *Smoke and spice in this sub-Alpine lightweight* |

NEW ZEALAND

£3.99	6	Tikki Ridge Dry White 2000	*Dry indeed – lots of citric acidity, a sort of Kiwi Muscadet*
£4.99	8	Azure Bay Chardonnay Semillon 2000	*Naff blue ('azure') bottle lets down a firm-fruited clean dry wine*
£4.99	9/10	Montana Riesling 2000	*Splendidly crisp-appley Riesling has creamy depths – a 'commercial' brand from NZ's biggest producer, but none the worse for that*
£5.99	10	Villa Maria Private Bin Riesling 2000	*Sweet-apple nose, a really racy, slaking limey wine of exciting style*
£6.49	10	Stoneleigh Vineyard Sauvignon Blanc 2000	*Grass, nettles, the whole wild garden on a dewy spring morning are all, no kidding, suggested by this cracking pure-fruit Marlborough masterpiece*
£6.99	9	Oyster Bay Marlborough Chardonnay 2000	*Happy mix of flinty freshness and sweet-apple lusciousness*
£7.99	9	Montana Reserve Barrique Fermented Chardonnay 1999	*Golden-coloured and opulently flavoured old-fashioned rich but balanced wine*
£7.99	9	Wither Hills Sauvignon Blanc 2000	*Fine, pure, gooseberry scented – balanced wine*
£8.99	8	Craggy Range Sauvignon Blanc 2000	*Ripe style (and 13.7% alcohol) with a distinct brassica nose – pleasing but untypical*
£8.99	8	Jackson Estate Sauvignon Blanc 2000	*Subtle, intense style with green acidity*

ROMANIA

| £3.49 | 9 | Willow Ridge Sauvignon Blanc Feteasca 2000 | *Gamey, vegetal nose is relishable as is tiny hint of caramel in the bottom flavour* |

SOUTH AFRICA

£3.29	9	Culemborg Cape White 2000	*Very cheap and rather a good fruit-salad sort of wine with clean finish*
£3.89	8	Diamond Hills Chenin Blanc/ Chardonnay 2000	*'Safe' clean blend is fresh and satisfying*
£3.99	8	Culemborg Unwooded Chardonnay 2000	*Clean, if a shade dilute, and refreshing*
£6.99	8	Springfield Special Cuvée Sauvignon Blanc 2000	*Nice nettly nose, big complete super-fresh crisp wine just short of tart – little bit pricy*
£7.99	10	Jordan Chardonnay 2000	*Outstanding butterscotch-scented pure-mineral-fruit Chardonnay of surpassing quality*
£7.99	9/10	Steenberg Sauvignon Blanc 2000	*Stylish gooseberry-scented sunny wine that searches out the tastebuds – special quality*
£7.99	9	Steenberg Semillon 2000	*Plush, pineapple-honey-scented dry white with purity and textbook finish*

SPAIN

£4.49	7	Lustau Moscatel de Chipiona	*Very sweet confection from famed sherry producer*
£4.69	9/10	Rueda, Palacio de Bornos, 2000	*Grassy-fresh nose with matching liveliness of flavour – 'Sauvignon-style' with real quality*
£5.99	9/10	CVNE Monopole Rioja Blanco 1998	*Lush vanillin smell and lavish oaky fruit in this rich but zesty white Rioja*
£7.99	9	Albariño Pazo de Seoane 2000	*Herbaceous (sage in there somewhere) character to this intense and exotic dry refresher from Rias Baixas region*

USA

£6.99   6   Bonterra Vineyards Muscat 1999   *A real curio from usually excellent Bonterra is sweet, but reminds one too much of pears in syrup*

Waitrose is among several supermarkets offering this stonking Sicilian dry white at £4.99 – it's a lot of wine for the money

PERSONAL NOTES:

....

....

....

....

....

....

....

WINE RACK

See Thresher

A brief vocabulary

Wine labels convey a lot of information, some of it helpful. Under a combination of UK and EU regulations, the quantity and alcoholic strength of the contents must be displayed, as must the country of origin. And besides the wines from the traditional regions and appellations of France (Bordeaux, Burgundy etc.), Italy (Barolo, Chianti etc.) and Spain (Rioja, Navarra) the label is also very likely to bear the name of the grape or grapes involved. In the mass market, grape names such as Chardonnay and Shiraz now count for a lot more than this or that vineyard, region or even nation.

So, this glossary includes the names of more than 50 different grape varieties along with brief descriptions of their characteristics. The varietal name on a label tells you more than anything else about what to expect of the wine.

Other items in this vocabulary, which does seem to expand alarmingly in each succeeding edition of *Best Wine Buys,* include short summaries of the regions and appellations of recommended wines and some of the many label designations given to the style, alleged quality and regulatory classification.

Finally, I have tried to explain in simple and rational terms the many peculiar words I use in trying to convey the characteristics of wines described. 'Delicious' might need no further qualification, but the likes of 'bouncy', 'green' and 'liquorous' probably do.

abboccato – Medium-dry white wine style. Italy, especially Orvieto.

AC – see **Appellation d'Origine Contrôlée.**

acidity – To be any good, every wine must have the right level of acidity. It gives wine the element of dryness or sharpness it needs to prevent cloying sweetness or dull wateriness. Too much acidity, and wine tastes raw or acetic (vinegary). Winemakers strive to create balanced acidity - either by cleverly controlling the natural processes, or by adding sugar and acid to correct imbalances.

aftertaste – The flavour that lingers in the mouth after swallowing the wine.

Aglianico – Black grape variety of southern Italy. It is romantically associated. When the ancient Greeks first colonised Italy in the 7th century BC with the prime purpose of planting it as a vineyard (Greek name for Italy was *Oenotria* - land of cultivated vines) the name for the vines the Greeks brought with them was Ellenico (as in *Hellas*, Greece), from which Aglianico is the modern rendering. To return to the point, these ancient vines, especially in the arid volcanic landscapes of Basilicata, produce excellent dark, earthy and highly distinctive wines. A name to look out for.

Agriculture Biologique – On French wine labels, an indication that the wine has been made by organic methods

Albariño – White grape variety of Spain makes intriguingly perfumed fresh and spicy dry wines, especially in esteemed Rias Baixas region.

Almansa – DO winemaking region of Spain inland from Alicante, making great-value red wines.

alcohol – The alcohol levels in wines are expressed in terms of alcohol by volume (abv). That is, the percentage of the volume of the wine that is common, or ethyl, alcohol. A typical wine at 12% abv is thus 12 parts alcohol and, in effect, 88 parts fruit juice.

The question of how much alcohol we can drink without harming ourselves in the short or long term is an impossible one to answer, but there is more or less general agreement among scientists that small amounts of alcohol are good for us, even if the only evidence of this is actuarial – the fact that mortality statistics show teetotallers live significantly shorter lives than moderate drinkers.

According to the Department of Health, there are 'safe limits' to the amount of alcohol we should drink weekly. These limits are measured in units of alcohol, with a small glass of wine taken to be one unit. Men are advised that 28 units a week is the most they can drink without risk to health, and for women (whose liver function differs from men because of metabolic differences) the figure is 21 units.

If you wish to measure your consumption closely, note that a standard 75cl bottle of wine at 12% alcohol contains 9 units. A bottle of German Moselle at 8% alcohol has only 6 units, but a bottle of Australian Chardonnay at 14% has 10.5.

Alentejo – Wine region of southern Portugal (immediately north of the Algarve) with a fast-improving reputation, especially for sappy, keen reds from local grapes varieties including Aragones, Castelão and Trincadeira grapes.

Alsace – France's easternmost wine-producing region lies between the Vosges mountains and the Rhine river, with Germany beyond. These conditions make for the production of some of the world's most delicious and fascinating white wines, always sold under the name of their constituent grapes. Pinot Blanc is the most affordable – and is well worth looking out for. The 'noble' grape varieties of the region are Gewürztraminer, Muscat, Riesling and Tokay Pinot Gris and they are always made on a single-variety basis. The richest, most exotic wines are those from individual *grand cru* vineyards which are named on the label. Some *vendange tardive* (late harvest) wines are made, but tend to be expensive. All the wines are sold in tall, slim green bottles known as *flûtes* that closely resemble those of the Mosel, and the names of producers and grape varieties are often German too, so it is widely assumed that Alsace wines are German in style, if not in nationality. But this is not the case in either particular. Alsace wines are dry and quite unique in character – and definitely French.

amontillado – see **sherry**

aperitif – If a wine is thus described, I believe it will give more pleasure before a meal than with one. Crisp, low-alcohol German wines and other delicately flavoured whites (including many dry Italians) are examples.

Appellation d'Origine Contrôlée – Commonly abbreviated to AC or AOC, it is the system under which quality wines are defined in France. About a third of the country's vast annual output qualifies, and there are more than 400 distinct AC zones. The declaration of an AC on the label signifies the wine meets standards concerning location of vineyards and wineries, grape varieties and limits on harvest per hectare, methods of cultivation and vinification, and alcohol content. Wines are inspected and tasted by state-appointed committees. The one major aspect of any given wine that an AC cannot guarantee is that you will like it – but it certainly improves the chances.

Apulia – Anglicised name for Puglia.

Ardèche – Region of southern France to the west of the Rhône valley, home to a good vin de pays zone known as the Coteaux de L'Ardèche. Lots of decent-value reds from Syrah grapes, and some, less-interesting, dry whites.

Asti – Town and major winemaking centre in Piedmont, Italy. The sparkling *(spumante)* sweet wines made from Moscato grapes are inexpensive and often delicious. Typical alcohol level is a modest 7%.

attack – In wine tasting, the first impression made by the wine in the mouth.

auslese – German wine-quality designation. See **QmP**.

backbone – A personal item of wine-tasting terminology. It's the impression given by a well-made wine in which the flavours are a pleasure to savour at all three stages: first sensation in the mouth; while being held in the mouth; in the aftertaste when the wine has been swallowed or spat out. Such a wine is held together by backbone.

Baga – Black grape variety indigenous to Portugal. Makes famously concentrated, juicy reds that get their deep colour from the grape's particularly thick skins. Look out for this name, now quite frequently quoted as the varietal on Portuguese wine labels. Often very good value for money.

balance – A big word in the vocabulary of wine tasting. Respectable wine must get two key things right: lots of fruitiness from the sweet grape juice, and plenty of acidity so the sweetness is 'balanced' with the crispness familiar in good dry whites and the dryness that marks out good reds. Some wines are noticeably 'well-balanced' in that they have memorable fruitiness and the clean, satisfying 'finish' (last flavour in the mouth) that ideal acidity imparts.

Barbera – Black grape variety originally of Piedmont in Italy. Most commonly seen as Barbera d'Asti, the vigorously fruity red wine made around Asti – which is better known for sweet sparkling Asti Spumante. Barbera grapes are now being grown in South America, often producing a sleeker, smoother style than at home in Italy.

Barossa Valley – Famed vineyard region north of Adelaide, Australia, produces hearty reds principally from Shiraz, Cabernet Sauvignon and Grenache grapes plus plenty of lush white wine from Chardonnay. Also known for limey, long-lived mineral dry whites from Riesling grapes.

barrique – Barrel in French. *En barrique* on a wine label signifies the wine has been matured in oak.

Beaujolais – Unique red wines from the southern reaches of Burgundy, France, are made from Gamay grapes. Beaujolais Nouveau, the new wine of each harvest, is released on the third Thursday of every November to much ballyhoo. It provides a friendly introduction to this deliciously bouncy, fleshly fruity wine style. Decent Beaujolais for enjoying during the rest of the year has lately become rather more expensive. If splashing out, go for Beaujolais Villages, from the region's better, northern vineyards.

There are ten AC zones within the northern part of the region making wines under their own names. Known as the *crus,* these are Brouilly, Chénas, Chiroubles, Côte de Brouilly, Fleurie, Juliénas, Morgon, Moulin à Vent, Regnié and St Amour and produce most of the very best wines of the region – at prices a pound or two higher than for Beaujolais Villages.

Beaumes de Venise – Village near Châteauneuf du Pape in France's Rhône valley famous for sweet and alcoholic wine from Muscat grapes. Delicious, grapy wines. A small number of growers also make strong (sometimes rather tough) red wines under the village name.

Beaune – One of the two winemaking centres (the other is Nuits St Georges) at the heart of Burgundy in France. Three of the region's humbler appellations take the name of the town: Côte de Beaune, Côte de Beaune-Villages and Hautes Côtes de Beaune. Wines made under these ACs are often, but by no means always, good value for money.

berry fruit – Some red wines deliver a burst of flavour in the mouth that corresponds to biting into a newly picked berry – strawberry, blackberry etc. So a wine described as having berry fruit (by this writer, anyway) has freshness, liveliness, immediate appeal.

bianco – White wine, Italy.

Bical – White grape variety principally of Dão region of northern Portugal. Not usually identified on labels, because most of it goes into inexpensive sparkling wines. Can make still wines of very refreshing crispness.

biodynamics – A cultivation method taking the organic approach several steps further. Biodynamic winemakers plant and tend their vineyards according to a date and time calendar 'in harmony' with the movements of the planets. Some of France's best-known wine estates subscribe, and many more are going that way. It might all sound bonkers, but it's salutary to learn that biodynamics is based on principles first described by a very eminent man, the Austrian educationist Rudolph Steiner. He's lately been in the news for having written, in 1919, that farmers crazy enough to feed animal products to cattle would drive those cattle 'mad'.

bite – In wine tasting, the impression on the palate of a wine with plenty of acidity and, often, tannin.

blanc – White wine, France.

blanc de blancs – White wine from white grapes, France. Seems to be stating the obvious, but some white wines (e.g. champagne) are made, partially or entirely, from black grapes.

blanc de noirs – White wine from black grapes, France. Usually sparkling (especially champagne) made from black Pinot Meunier and Pinot Noir grapes, with no Chardonnay or other white varieties.

blanco – White wine, Spain and Portugal.

Blauer Zweigelt – Black grape variety of Austria, making a large proportion of the country's red wines, some of excellent quality.

bodega – In Spain, a wine producer or wine shop.

Bonarda – Black grape variety of northern Italy. Now more widely planted in Argentina, where it makes rather elegant red wines, often representing great value.

botrytis – Full name, *botrytis cinerea,* is that of a beneficent fungus that can attack ripe grape bunches late in the season, shrivelling the berries to a gruesome-looking mess which yields concentrated juice of prized sweetness. Cheerfully known as 'noble rot', this fungus is actively encouraged by winemakers in regions as diverse as Sauternes (in Bordeaux), Monbazillac (in Bergerac), the Rhine and Mosel valleys and South Australia to make ambrosial 'dessert' wines.

bouncy – The feel in the mouth of a red wine with young, juicy fruitiness. Good Beaujolais is bouncy as are many northwest-Italian wines from Barbera and Dolcetto grapes.

Bourgogne Grand Ordinaire – Appellation of France's Burgundy region for 'ordinary' red wines from either Gamay or Pinot Noir grapes, or both. Some good-value wines, especially from the Buxy Co-operative in the southern Chalonnais area.

Bourgueil – Appellation of Loire Valley, France. Long-lived red wines from Cabernet Franc grapes.

briary – In wine tasting, associated with the flavours of fruit from prickly bushes such as blackberries.

brûlé – Pleasant burnt-toffee taste or smell, as in crème brûlée.

brut – Driest style of sparkling wine. Originally French, for very dry champagnes specially developed for the British market, but now used for sparkling wines from all round the world.

Buzet – Little-seen AC of southwest France overshadowed by Bordeaux but producing some characterful ripe reds.

Cabardès – New AC (1998) for red and rosé wines from area north of Carcassonne, Aude, France. Principally Cabernet Sauvignon and Merlot grapes.

Cabernet Franc – Black grape variety originally of France. It makes the light-bodied and keenly-edged red wines of the Loire Valley – such as Chinon and Saumur. And it is much grown in Bordeaux, especially in the appellation of St Emilion. Also now planted in Argentina, Australia and North America. Wines, especially in the Loire, are characterised by a leafy, sappy style and bold fruitiness. Most are best enjoyed young.

Cabernet Sauvignon – Black (or, rather, blue) grape variety now grown in virtually every wine-producing nation on earth. When perfectly ripened, the grapes are smaller than many other varieties and have particularly thick skins. This means that when pressed Cabernet grapes have a high proportion of skin to juice – and that makes for wine with lots of colour and tannin *(qv)*. In Bordeaux, the grape's traditional home, the grandest Cabernet-based wines have always been known as *vins de garde* (wines to keep) because they take years, even decades, to evolve as the effect of all that skin extraction preserves the fruit all the way to magnificent maturity. But in today's impatient world, these grapes are exploited in modern winemaking techniques to produce the sublime flavours of mature Cabernet without having to hang around for lengthy periods awaiting maturation. While there's nothing like a fine, ten-year-old claret (and nothing quite as expensive) there are many excellent Cabernets from around the world that amply illustrate this grape's characteristics. Classic smells and flavours include blackcurrants, cedar wood, chocolate, tobacco – even violets.

Cahors – An AC of the Lot Valley in south-west France once famous for 'black wine'. This was a curious concoction of straightforward wine mixed with a soupy must made by boiling up new-pressed juice to concentrate it (through evaporation) before fermentation. The myth is still perpetuated that Cahors wine continues to be in this way, but production on this basis actually ceased 150 years ago. Cahors today is no stronger, or blacker, than the wines of neighbouring appellations.

Calatayud – DO (quality wine zone) near Zaragoza in the Aragon region of northern Spain where they're making some astonishingly good wines at bargain prices, mainly reds from Garnacha and Tempranillo grapes. These are the varieties that go into the light and oaky wines of Rioja, but in Calatayud, the wines are dark, dense and decidedly different.

cantina sociale – See **co-op.**

Carignan – Black grape variety of Mediterranean France. It is rarely identified on labels, but is a major constituent of wines from the southern Rhône and Languedoc-Roussillon regions, especially the cheaper brands. Known as Carignano in Italy and Cariñena in Spain.

Carmenère – Black grape variety once widely grown in Bordeaux but abandoned due to cultivation problems. Lately revived in South America where it is producing fine wines.

cassis – As a tasting note, signifies a wine has a noticeable blackcurrant-concentrate flavour or smell. Much associated with the Cabernet Sauvignon grape.

Castelao – Portuguese black grape variety. Same as Periquita.

Catarratto – White grape variety of Sicily. In skilled hands it makes keen, green-fruit dry whites. Also used for marsala.

Cava – The sparkling wine of Spain. Most originates in Catalonia, but the Denominacion de Origen guarantee of authenticity is open to producers in many regions of the country. Although much cava is very reasonably priced, don't assume it's greatly inferior to the more expensive wines of Champagne. Cava is made by the same method as champagne (second fermentation in bottle – known in Spain as the *metodo classico*) and can compete very well for value.

cépage – Grape variety, French. 'Cépage Merlot' on a label simply means the wine is made largely or exclusively from Merlot grapes.

Chablis – Northernmost AC of France's Burgundy region. Its dry white wines from Chardonnay grapes are known for their fresh and steely style, but the best wines also age very gracefully into complex classics.

Chardonnay – The world's most-popular grape variety. Said to originate from the village of Chardonnay in the Mâconnais region of southern Burgundy, the vine is now planted in every wine-producing nation. Wines are commonly characterised by generous colour and sweet-apple smell, but styles range from lean and sharp to opulently rich. Australia started the craze for oaked Chardonnay, the gold-coloured, super-ripe, buttery 'upfront' wines that are a caricature of lavish and outrageously expensive Burgundies such as Meursault and Puligny-Montrachet. Rich to the point of egginess, these Ozzie pretenders are now giving way to a sleeker, more minerally style with much less oak presence – if any at all. California and Chile, New Zealand and South Africa are competing hard to imitate the Burgundian style, and Australia's success in doing so.

Châteauneuf-du-Pape – Famed appellation centred on a picturesque village of the southern Rhône valley in France where in the 1320s French Pope Clement V had a splendid 'new château' built for himself as a country retreat amidst his vineyards. The red wines of the AC, which can be made from 13 different grape varieties but principally Grenache, Syrah and Mourvèdre, are regarded as the best of the southern Rhône and have become rather expensive – but they can be sensationally good. Expensive white wines are also made.

Chenin Blanc – White grape variety of the Loire Valley, France. Now also grown farther afield, especially in South Africa. Makes dry, soft white wines and also rich, sweet styles. Sadly, many low-cost Chenin wines are bland and uninteresting.

cherry – In wine-tasting, either a pale red colour or, more commonly, a smell or flavour akin to the sun-warmed, bursting sweet ripeness of cherries. Many Italian wines from lightweights such as Bardolino and Valpolicella to serious Chianti, have this character. 'Black cherry' as a description is often used of Merlot wines – meaning they are sweet but have a firmness associated with the thicker skins of black cherries.

Cinsault – Black grape variety of southern France, where it is invariably blended with others in wines of all qualities ranging from vin de pays to the pricy reds of Châteauneuf du Pape. Also much-planted in South Africa. The effect in wine is to add keen aromas (sometimes compared with turpentine!) and softness to the blend. The name is often spelt Cinsaut.

Clape, La – A small *cru* (defined quality-vineyard area) within the Coteaux du Languedoc where the growers make some seriously delicious red wines, mainly from Carignan, Grenache and Syrah grapes. A name worth looking out for on labels from the region.

claret – The red wine of Bordeaux, France. It comes from Latin *clarus,* meaning clear, recalling a time when the red wines of the region were much lighter in colour than they are now.

clarete – On Spanish labels indicates a pale-coloured red wine. *Tinto* signifies a deeper hue.

classic – An overused term in every respect – wine descriptions being no exception. In this book, the word is used to describe a very good wine of its type. So, a 'classic' Cabernet Sauvignon is one that is recognisably and admirably characteristic of that grape.

Classico – Under Italy's wine laws, this word appended to the name of a DOC zone has an important significance. The Classico wines of the region can only be made from vineyards lying in the best-rated areas, and wines thus labelled (e.g. Chianti Classico, Soave Classico, Valpolicella Classico) can be reliably counted on to be a cut above the rest.

Colombard – White grape variety of southern France. Once employed almost entirely for making the wine that is distilled for armagnac and cognac brandies, but lately restored to varietal prominence in the vin de pays des Côtes de Gascogne where hi-tech wineries turn it into a fresh and crisp, if unchallenging, dry wine at a budget price. But beware, cheap Colombard (especially from South Africa) can still be very dull.

concept wines – A marketing term now very much part of the wine vocabulary. More and more wines are labelled with names portraying a concept rather than indicating the nature of the wine itself. Examples are 'Winds of Change' wines from South Africa, celebrating the post-Apartheid era.

co-op – Very many of France's good-quality, inexpensive wines are made by co-operatives. These are wine-producing factories whose members, and joint-owners, are local *vignerons* (vine-growers). Each year they sell their harvests to the co-op for turning into branded wines. In Italy, co-op wines can be identified by the words *Cantina Sociale* on the label and in Germany by the term *Winzergenossenschaft.*

Corbières – A name to look out for. It's an AC of France's Midi (deep south) and produces countless robust reds and a few interesting whites, often at bargain prices.

Cortese – Obscure white grape variety of Piedmont, Italy. At its best, makes amazingly delicious, keenly brisk and fascinating wines. Worth seeking out.

Costières de Nîmes – An AC of Languedoc-Roussillon in southern France. It's a name to look out for, the best red wines being notable for their concentration of colour and fruit, with the earthy-spiciness of the better Rhône wines and a likeable liquorice note.

côte – In French, it simply means a side, or slope – of a hill. The implication in wine terms is that the grapes come from a vineyard ideally situated for maximum sunlight, good drainage and the unique soil conditions prevailing on the hill in question. It's fair enough to claim that vines grown on slopes might get more sunlight than those grown on the flat, but there is no guarantee whatsoever that any wine labelled 'Côtes du' this or that is made from grapes grown on a hillside anyway. Côtes du Rhône wines are a case in point. Many 'côtes' wines come from entirely level vineyards and it is worth remembering that many of the vineyards of Bordeaux, producing most of the world's priciest wines, are little short of prairie flat. The quality factor is determined much more significantly by the weather and the talents of the winemaker.

Côtes du Rhône – One of the biggest and best-known appellations of France, covering an area roughly defined by the southern reaches of the valley of the river Rhône. Notorious for cheap and execrable reds, the Côtes du Rhône AC does also produce some brilliant-value warm and spicy reds, principally from Grenache and Syrah grapes. There are some white and rosé wines.

Côtes du Rhône Villages – Appellation within the larger Côtes du Rhône AC for wine of supposed superiority made in a number of zones associated with a long list of nominated individual villages. Villages wines may be more interesting than their humbler counterparts, but this cannot be counted on.

Côtes du Roussillon – Huge appellation of southwest France known for strong, dark, peppery reds often offering very decent value.

Côtes du Roussillon Villages – Appellation for superior wines from a number of nominated locations within the larger Roussillon AC. Some of these village wines can be of exceptional quality and value.

crianza – Means 'nursery' in Spanish. On Rioja and Navarra wines, the designation signifies a wine that has been nursed through a maturing period of at least a year in oak casks and a further six months in bottle before being released for sale.

cru – A word that crops up with confusing regularity on French wine labels. It means 'the growing' or 'the making' of a wine and asserts that the wine concerned is from a specific vineyard. Under the Appellation Contrôlée rules, countless *crus* are classified in various hierarchical ranks. Hundreds of individual vineyards are described as *premier cru* or *grand cru* in the classic wine regions of Alsace, Bordeaux, Burgundy and Champagne. The common denominator in all these is that the wine can be counted on to be enormously expensive. On humbler wines, the use of the word 'cru' tends to be mere decoration.

cuvée – French for the wine in a *cuve* or vat. The word is much used on labels to imply that the wine is from just one vat, and thus of unique, unblended character. *Premier cuvée* is supposedly the best wine from a given pressing because the grapes have had only the initial, gentle squashing to extract the free-run juice. Subsequent *cuvées* will have been from harsher pressings, grinding the grape pulp to extract the last drop of juice.

demi sec – 'Half-dry' style of French (and some other) wines. Beware. It can mean anything from off-dry to cloyingly sweet.

DO – Denominacion de Origen, Spain's wine-regulating scheme, similar to France's AC, but older – the first DO region was Rioja, from 1926. DO wines are Spain's best, accounting for a third of the annual crop.

DOC – Stands for Denominazione di Origine Controllata, Italy's equivalent of France's AC. The wines are made according to the stipulations of each of its 280 denominated zones of origin, 20 of which enjoy the superior classification of DOCG (DOC with e Garantita appended).

earthy – A tricky word in the wine vocabulary. In this book, its use is meant to be complimentary. It indicates that the wine somehow suggests the soil the grapes were grown in, even (perhaps a shade too poetically) the landscape in which the vineyards lie. The amazing-value red wines of the torrid, volcanic southernmost regions of Italy are often described as earthy. This is an association with the pleasantly 'scorched' back-flavour in wines made from the ultra-ripe harvests of this near-sub-tropical part of the world.

edge – A wine with edge is one with evident (not excessive) acidity.

élevé – 'Brought up' in French. Much used on wine labels where the wine has been matured (brought up) in oak barrels *(Elevé en fûts de chêne)* to give it extra dimensions.

Entre Deux Mers – Meaning 'between two seas', it's a region lying between the Dordogne and Garonne rivers of Bordeaux, now mainly known for dry white wines from Sauvignon and Semillon grapes. Quality rarely seems exciting.

Estremadura – Wine-producing region occupying Portugal's coastal area north of Lisbon. Lots of interesting wines from indigenous grape varieties, usually at bargain prices. If a label mentions Estremadura, it is a safe rule that there might be something good within.

Faugères – AC of the Languedoc in southwest France. Source of many hearty, economic reds.

Feteasca – White grape variety widely grown in Romania. Name means 'maiden's grape' and the wine tends to be soft and slightly sweet.

finish – The last flavour lingering in the mouth after wine has been swallowed.

fino – Pale and very dry style of sherry. You drink it thoroughly chilled – and you don't keep it any longer after opening than other dry white wines. Needs to be fresh to be at its best.

Fitou – One of the first 'designer' wines, it's an appellation in France's Languedoc region, where production is dominated by one huge co-operative, the Vignerons de Mont Tauch. Back in the 1970s, this co-op paid a corporate-image company to come up with a Fitou logo and label-design style, and the wines have prospered ever since. And it's not just packaging – Fitou at all price levels can be very good value, especially from the Mont Tauch co-op.

flabby – Fun word describing a wine that tastes dilute or watery, with insufficient acidity.

flying winemaker – Back-labels on supermarket wines sometimes boast that the contents are made by a flying winemaker. They're consultants who visit vineyards worldwide at harvest time to oversee the production process, perhaps to ensure that the style of wine wanted by a major customer (usually a supermarket) is adhered to by the locals. These people are very often Australian, with degrees in oenology (the science of winemaking) and well up on latest technology and biochemistry. If there is a criticism of flying winemakers it is that they have a tendency to impose a uniform style on all the vineyards upon which they descend. Thus, more and more French, Italian and Spanish wines, for example, are starting to take on the 'upfront fruitiness' of the wines of Australia.

fruit – In tasting terms, the fruit is the greater part of the overall flavour of a wine. The wine is (or should be) after all, composed entirely of fruit.

Gamay – The black grape that makes all red Beaujolais. It is a pretty safe rule to avoid Gamay wines from any other region. It's a grape that does not do well elsewhere.

Garganega – White grape variety of the Veneto region of northwest Italy. Best known as the principal ingredient of Soave, but occasionally included in varietal blends and mentioned as such on labels. Correctly pronounced 'gar GAN iger'.

Gewürztraminer – One of the great grape varieties of Alsace, France. At their best, the wines are perfumed with lychees and are richly, spicily fruity, yet quite dry. Gewürztraminer from Alsace is almost always expensive – never under £5 – but the grape is also grown with some success in Eastern Europe, Germany, Italy and South America, and sold at more approachable prices. Pronounced 'geh VOORTS tram eéner'.

Graciano - Black grape variety of Spain is one of the minor constituents of Rioja. Better known in its own right in Australia where it can make dense, spicy long-lived red wines.

green - In flavour, a wine that is unripe and raw-tasting.

grip - In wine-tasting terminology, the sensation in the mouth produced by a wine that has a healthy quantity of tannin in it. A wine with grip is a good wine. A wine with too much tannin, or which is still too young (the tannin hasn't 'softened' with age) is not described as having grip, but as mouth-puckering - or simply undrinkable.

Grüner Veltliner - The 'national' white-wine grape of Austria. In the past it made mostly soft, German-style everyday wines, but now is behind some excellent dry styles, too.

halbtrocken - 'Half-dry' in Germany's wine vocabulary. A reassurance that the wine is not some ghastly sugared Liebfraumilch-style confection.

hock - The wine of Germany's Rhine river valleys. It comes in brown bottles, as distinct from the wine of the Mosel river valleys - which comes in green ones.

Indicazione Geografica Tipica - Italy's recently instituted wine-quality designation, broadly equivalent to France's vin de pays. The label has to state the geographical location of the vineyard and will often (but not always) state the principal grape varieties from which the wine is made.

Inycon - A new wine brand of Sicily's huge Settesoli co-operative and the label on several of the highest-rated wines in this book. Inycon was the Ancient Greek name of the modern Sicilian village of Menfi where the vineyards and winery for this remarkable brand have been established.

jammy - the 'sweetness' in dry red wines is supposed to evoke ripeness rather than sugariness. Sometimes, flavours include a sweetness reminiscent of jam. Usually a fault in the winemaking technique.

joven - Young wine, Spanish. In regions such as Rioja, *vino joven* is a synonym for *sin crianza*, 'without ageing' in cask or bottle.

Kabinett - Under Germany's bewildering wine-quality rules, this is a classification of a top-quality (**QmP** - *qv*) wine. Expect a keen, dry, racy style. The name comes from the cabinet or cupboard in which winemakers traditionally kept their most treasured bottles.

Kekfrankos - Black grape variety of Hungary, particularly the Sopron region, which makes some of the country's more interesting red wines, characterised by colour and spiciness. Same variety as Austria's Blaufrankisch.

Languedoc-Roussillon – Vast area of southern France, including the country's south-west Mediterranean region. The source, now, of many great-value wines from countless ACs and vin de pays zones.

legs – The liquid residue left clinging to the sides of the glass after wine has been swirled. The persistence of the legs is an indicator of the weight of alcohol. Also known as 'tears'.

liquorice – The pungent slightly burnt flavours of this once-fashionable confection are detectable in some wines made from very ripe grapes, for example the Malbec harvested in Argentina and several varieties grown in the very hot vineyards of southernmost Italy. A close synonym is 'tarry'. This characteristic is by no means a fault in red wine, unless very dominant, but it can make for a challenging flavour that might not appeal to all tastes.

liquorous – Wines of great weight and glyceriney texture (evidenced by the 'legs' or 'tears' which cling to the glass after the wine has been swirled) are always noteworthy. The connection with liquor is drawn in respect of the feel of the wine in the mouth, rather than with the higher alcoholic strength of spirits.

Macabeo – One of the main grapes used for cava, the sparkling wine of Spain. It is the same grape as Viura.

Mâcon – Town and collective appellation of southern Burgundy, France. Lightweight white wines from Chardonnay grapes and similarly light reds from Pinot Noir and some Gamay. The better ones, and the ones exported, have the AC Mâcon-Villages and there are individual-village wines with their own ACs including Mâcon-Clessé, Mâcon-Viré and Mâcon-Lugny.

Malbec – Black grape variety grown on a small scale in Bordeaux, and the mainstay of the wines of Cahors in France's Dordogne region under the name Cot. Now much better known for producing big butch reds in Argentina.

Mantinia – Winemaking region of the Peloponnese, Greece. Dry whites from Moschofilero grapes are aromatic and refreshing.

Manzanilla – Pale, very dry sherry of Sanlucar de Barrameida, a grungy seaport on the southernmost coast of Spain. Manzanilla is proud to be distinct from the pale, very dry fino sherry of the main producing town of Jerez de la Frontera down the coast. Drink it chilled and fresh – it goes downhill in an opened bottle after just a few days, even if kept (as it should be) in the fridge.

Margaret River – Vineyard region of Western Australia regarded as ideal for grape varieties including Cabernet Sauvignon. It is has a relatively cool climate and a reputation for making sophisticated wines, both red and white.

Marlborough – Best-known vineyard region of New Zealand's South Island has a cool climate and a name for brisk but cerebral Sauvignon and Chardonnay wines.

Marsanne – White grape variety of the northern Rhône Valley and, increasingly, of the wider south of France. It's known for making well-coloured wines with heady aroma and fruit.

Mataro – Black grape variety of Australia. It's the same as the Mourvèdre of France.

McLaren Vale – Vineyard region south of Adelaide in SE Australia. Known for serious-quality wines from grape varieties including Shiraz and Chardonnay.

meaty – Weighty, rich red wine style.

Mendoza – The region to watch in Argentina. Lying to the east of the Andes mountains, just about opposite the best vineyards of Chile on the other side, Mendoza accounts for the bulk of Argentine wine production, with quality improving fast.

Merlot – One of the great black wine grapes of Bordeaux, and now grown all over the world. Characteristics of Merlot-based wines attract descriptions such as 'plummy' and 'plump' with black-cherry aroma. The grapes are larger than most, and thus have less skin in proportion to their flesh. This means the resulting wines have less tannin than wines from smaller-berry varieties such as Cabernet Sauvignon, and are therefore, in the Bordeaux context at least, more suitable for drinking while still relatively young.

middle palate – In wine-tasting, the impression given by the wine when it is held in the mouth.

Midi – Catch-all term for the deep south of France west of the Rhône Valley.

mineral – Good dry white wines can have a crispness and freshness that somehow evokes this word. Purity of flavour is a key.

Minervois – AC for (mostly) red wines from vineyards around the town of Minerve in the Languedoc-Roussillon region of France. Often good value.

Monbazillac – AC for sweet 'dessert' wines within the wider appellation of Bergerac in southwest France. Made from the same grape varieties (principally Sauvignon and Semillon) that go into the much costlier counterpart wines of Barsac and Sauternes near Bordeaux, these stickies from botrytis-affected, late-harvested grapes can be delicious and good value for money.

Monastrell – Black grape variety of Spain, widely planted in Mediterranean regions for inexpensive wines notable for their high alcohol and toughness – though they can mature into excellent, soft reds. The variety is known in France as Mourvèdre and in Australia as Mataro.

Montalcino – Hilltown of Tuscany, Italy, and a DOCG for strong and very long-lived red wines from Brunello grapes. The wines are mostly very expensive. Rosso di Montalcino, a DOC for the humbler wines of the zone, is often a good buy.

Montepulciano – Black grape variety of Italy. Best-known in Montepulciano d'Abruzzo, the juicy, purply-black and bramble-fruited red of the Abruzzi region mid-way down Italy's Adriatic side. Also the grape in the rightly popular hearty reds of Rosso Conero from around Ancona in the Marches. Not to be confused with the hilltown of Montepulciano in Tuscany, famous for expensive Vino Nobile di Montepulciano wine.

morello – Lots of red wines have smells and flavours redolent of cherries. Morello cherries, among the darkest-coloured and sweetest of all varieties and the preferred choice of cherry-brandy producers, have a distinct sweetness resembled by some wines made from Merlot grapes. A morello whiff or taste is generally very welcome.

Moselle – The wine of Germany's Mosel river valleys, collectively known for winemaking purposes as Mosel-Saar-Ruwer. The wine always comes in slim, green bottles, as distinct from the brown bottles employed for Rhine wines.

Moscatel – Spanish Muscat.

Moscato – See **Muscat**.

Mourvèdre – Widely planted black grape variety of southern France. It's an ingredient in many of the wines of Provence, the Rhône and Languedoc, including the ubiquitous Vin de Pays d'Oc. It's a hot-climate vine and the wine is usually blended with other varieties to give sweet aromas and 'backbone' to the mix. Known as Mataro in Australia and Monastrell in Spain.

Muscadet – One of France's best-known everyday whites. It comes from vineyards at the estuarial end of the river Loire, and at its best has something of a sea-breezy freshness about it. The better wines are reckoned to be those from the vineyards in the Sèvre et Maine region, and many are made *sur lie* – 'on the lees' – meaning that the wine is left in contact with the yeasty deposit of its fermentation until just before bottling, in an endeavour to add interest to what can sometimes be an acidic and fruitless style.

Muscat – Grape variety with origins in ancient Greece, and still grown widely among the Aegean islands for the production of sweet white wines. Muscats are the wines that taste more like grape-juice than any other – but the high sugar levels ensure they are also among the most alcoholic of wines, too. Known as Moscato in Italy, the grape is much used for making sweet sparkling wines, as in Asti Spumante or Moscato d'Asti. There are several appellations in southwest France for inexpensive Muscats made rather like port, part-fermented before the addition of grape alcohol to halt the conversion of sugar into alcohol, creating a sweet and heady *vin doux naturel.* Dry Muscat wines, when well made, have a delicious sweet aroma but a refreshing light touch with flavours reminiscent variously of orange blossom, wood smoke and grapefruit!

must – New-pressed grape juice prior to fermentation.

Navarra – DO (Denominacion de Origen) wine-producing region of northern Spain adjacent to, and overshadowed by, Rioja. Navarra's wines can be startlingly akin to their neighbouring rivals, and sometimes rather better value for money.

négociant – In France, a dealer-producer who buys wines from growers and matures and/or blends them for sale under his own label. Purists can be a bit sniffy about these entrepreneurs, claiming that only the vine-grower with his or her own winemaking set-up can make truly authentic stuff, but the truth is that many of the best wines of France are négociant-produced – especially at the humbler end of the price scale. Négociants are often identified on wine labels as négociant-éleveur (literally 'dealer-bringer-up') and meaning that the wine has been matured, blended and bottled by the party in question.

Negro Amaro – Black grape variety mainly of Apulia, the fast-improving wine region of southeast Italy. Dense earthy red wines with ageing potential and plenty of alcohol. The grape behind Copertino.

Nero d'Avola – Black grape variety of Sicily and southern Italy. It makes deep-coloured wines which, given half a chance, can develop intensity and richness with age.

non-vintage – A wine is described as such when it has been blended from the harvests of more than one year. A non-vintage wine is not necessarily an inferior one, but under quality-control regulations around the world, still table wines most usually derive solely from one year's grape crop to qualify for appellation status. Champagnes and sparkling wines are mostly blended from several vintages, as are fortified wines such as basic port and sherry.

nose – In the vocabulary of the wine taster, the nose is the scent of a wine. Sounds a bit dotty, but makes a sensible-enough alternative to the rather bald 'smell'. The use of the word 'perfume' implies that the wine smells particularly good. 'Aroma' is used specifically to describe a wine that smells as it should, as in 'this Burgundy has the authentic strawberry-raspberry aroma of Pinot Noir' (see **Pinot Noir**).

Oltrepo Pavese – Wine-producing zone of Piedmont, northwest Italy. The name means 'south of Pavia across the [river] Po' and the wines, both white and red, can be excellent quality and value for money.

organic wine – As in other sectors of the food industry, demand for organically made wine is – or appears to be – growing. As a rule, a wine qualifies as organic if it comes entirely from grapes grown in vineyards cultivated without the use of synthetic materials, and made in a winery where chemical treatments or additives are shunned with similar vigour. In fact, there are plenty of winemakers in the world using organic methods, but who disdain to label their bottles as such. Wines that do brazenly proclaim their organic status tend to carry the same sort of premium as their counterparts round the corner in the fruit, vegetable and meat aisles. The upshot is that there is a very limited choice of organic wine at under a fiver. There is no single worldwide (or even Europe-wide) standard for organic food or wine, so you pretty much have to take the producer's word for it.

Periquita – Black grape variety of southern Portugal. Makes rather exotic spicy reds. Name means parrot.

Petite Sirah – Black grape variety of California and Latin America known for plenty of colour and long life. Not related to the Syrah of the Rhône.

Petit Verdot – Black grape variety of Bordeaux used to give additional colour, density and spiciness to Cabernet Sauvignon-dominated blends. Strictly a minority player at home, but in Australia and California it is grown as the principal variety for some big hearty reds of real character.

petrol – When white wines from certain grapes, especially Riesling, are allowed to age in the bottle for a year or two, they can take on a spirity aroma reminiscent of petrol or diesel. In grand mature German wines, this is considered a very good thing.

Picpoul de Pinet – Obscure white grape variety of the southern Rhône region of France occasionally makes interesting floral dry whites.

Pinotage – South Africa's own black grape variety. Makes red wines ranging from light and juicy to dark, strong and long-lived. It's a cross between Pinot Noir and a grape the South Africans used to call the Hermitage (thus the portmanteau name) but turns out to have been the Cinsault. Cheaper Pinotages tend to disappoint, but there has been an improvement in the standard of wines tasted during the year 2000.

Pinot Blanc – White grape variety principally of Alsace, France. Florally perfumed, exotically fruity dry white wines.

Pinot Grigio – White grape variety of northern Italy. Wines bearing its name have become fashionable in recent times. Good wines have an interesting smoky-pungent aroma and keen, slaking fruit. But most are dull. Originally a French grape, there known as Pinot Gris, which is renowned for making lushly exotic – and expensive – white wines in the Alsace region.

Pinot Noir – The great black grape of Burgundy, France. It makes all the region's fabulously expensive red wines. Notoriously difficult to grow in warmer climates, it is nevertheless cultivated by countless intrepid winemakers in the New World intent on reproducing the magic appeal of red Burgundy. California and New Zealand have come closest, but rarely at prices much below those for the real thing. Some Chilean and Romanian Pinot Noirs are inexpensive and worth trying.

Pouilly Fuissé – Village and AC of the Mâconnais region of southern Burgundy in France. Dry white wines from Chardonnay grapes. Wines are among the highest-rated of the Mâconnais.

Pouilly Fumé – Village and AC of the Loire Valley in France. Dry white wines from Sauvignon Blanc grapes. Similar 'pebbly', 'grassy' or even 'gooseberry' style to neighbouring AC Sancerre. The notion put about by some enthusiasts that Pouilly Fumé is 'smoky' is surely nothing more than word-association with the name.

Primitivo – Black grape variety of southern Italy, especially the region of Apulia/Puglia. The wines are typically dense and dark in colour with plenty of alcohol, and have an earthy, spicy style. Often a real bargain. It is closely related to California's Zinfandel, which makes purple, brambly wines of a very different hue.

Prosecco – White grape variety of Italy's Veneto region which gives its name to a light, sparkling and cheap wine that is much appreciated locally, but not widely exported.

Puglia – The region occupying the 'heel' of southern Italy, and one of the world's fastest-improving sources of inexpensive wines. Modern winemaking techniques and large regional grants from the EU are at least partly responsible.

QbA – On a German wine label stands for *Qualitätswein bestimmter Anbaugebebiet.* It means 'quality wine from designated areas' and implies that the wine is made from grapes with a minimum level of ripeness, but it's by no means a guarantee of exciting quality. Only wines labelled QmP (see next entry) can be depended upon to be special.

QmP – On a German wine label it stands for *Qualitätswein mit Prädikat.* These are the serious wines of Germany, made without the addition of sugar to 'improve' them. To qualify for QmP status, the grapes must reach a level of ripeness as measured on a sweetness scale – all according to Germany's fiendishly complicated wine-quality regulations. Wines from grapes that reach the stated minimum level of sweetness qualify for the description of Kabinett. The next level up earns the rank of Spätlese, meaning 'late-picked'. Kabinett wines can be expected to be dry and brisk in style, and Spätlese wines a little bit riper and fuller. The next grade up, Auslese, meaning 'selected harvest', indicates a wine made from super-ripe grapes; it will be golden in colour and honeyed in flavour. A generation ago, these wines were as valued, and as expensive, as any of the world's grandest appellations, but the collapse in demand for German wines in the UK – brought about by the disrepute rightly earned for floods of filthy Liebfraumilch – means they are now seriously undervalued. Majestic has an unrivalled range of great bargains from Germany.

Quincy – AC of Loire Valley, France, known for pebbly-dry white wines from Sauvignon grapes. The wines are forever compared to those of nearby and much better-known Sancerre – and Quincy often represents better value for money. Pronounced 'KAN see'.

Quinta – Portuguese for farm or estate. It precedes the names of many of Portugal's best-known wines. It is pronounced 'KEEN ta'.

racy – Evocative wine-tasting description for wine that thrills the tastebuds with a rush of exciting sensations. Good Rieslings often qualify.

raisiny – Wines from grapes that have been very ripe or overripe at harvest can take on a smell and flavour akin to the concentrated, heat-dried sweetness of raisins. As a minor element in the character of a wine, this can add to the appeal but as a dominant characteristic it is a fault.

Reserva – In Portugal and Spain, this has genuine significance. The Portuguese use it for special wines with a higher alcohol level and longer ageing, although the precise periods vary between regions. In Spain, especially in the Navarra and Rioja regions, it means the wine must have had at least a year in oak and two in bottle before release.

reserve – On French (as *Réserve*) or other wines, this implies special-quality, longer-aged wines, but has no official significance.

Retsina – The universal white wine of Greece. It has been traditionally made in Attica, the region of Athens, for a very long time, and is said to owe its origins and name to the ancient custom of sealing amphorae (terracotta jars) of the wine with a gum made from pine resin. Some of the flavour of the resin inevitably transmitted itself into the wine, and ancient Greeks acquired a lasting taste for it.

Reuilly – AC of Loire Valley, France, for crisp dry whites from Sauvignon grapes. Pronounced 'RUH yee'.

Ribatejo – Emerging wine region of Portugal. Worth seeking out on labels of red wines.

Riesling – The noble grape variety of Germany. It is correctly pronounced 'REEZ ling', not 'RICE ling'. Once notorious as the grape behind all those boring 'medium' Liebfraumilches and Niersteiners, this grape has had a bad press. In fact, there has never been much, if any, Riesling in Germany's cheap-and-nasty plonks. But the country's best wines, the so-called *Qualitätswein mit Prädikat* grades (see **QmP**), are made almost exclusively with Riesling. These wines range from crisply fresh and appley styles to extravagantly fruity, honeyed wines from late-harvested grapes. Excellent Riesling wines are also made in Alsace and now in Australia.

Rioja – The principal fine-wine region of Spain, in the country's north-east. The pricier wines are noted for their vanilla-pod richness from long ageing in oak casks. Younger wines, labelled variously *joven* (young) and *sin-crianza* (meaning they are without barrel-ageing – see **crianza**), are cheaper and can make relishable drinking.

Riserva – In Italy, a wine made only in the best vintages, and allowed longer ageing in cask and bottle.

Rivaner – Alternative name for Germany's Müller-Thurgau grape, the life-blood of Liebfraumilch.

rosso – Red wine, Italy.

Rosso Conero – DOC red wine made in the environs of Ancona in the Marches, Italy. Made from the Montepulciano grape, the wine can provide excellent value for money.

Ruby Cabernet – Black grape variety of California, created by crossing Cabernet Sauvignon and Carignan. Makes soft and squelchy red wine at home and in South Africa.

Rueda – DO of northwest Spain making first-class refreshing dry whites from the Verdejo grape. Exciting quality and prices, so far, are keen.

Salento – Up and coming wine region of southern Italy. Many good bargain reds from local grapes including Nero D'Avola and Primitivo.

Sancerre – Appellation Contrôlée of the Loire Valley, France, renowned for flinty-fresh Sauvignon whites and rarer Pinot Noir reds. These wines are never cheap, and recent tastings make it plain that only the best-made, individual-producer wines are worth the money. Budget brands seem mostly dull.

Sangiovese – The local black grape of Tuscany, Italy. It is the principal variety used for Chianti and is now widely planted in Latin America – often making delicious, Chianti-like wines with characteristic cherryish-but-deeply-ripe fruit and a dry, clean finish. Chianti wines have become (unjustifiably) expensive in recent years and cheaper Italian wines such as those called Sangiovese di Toscana make a consoling substitute.

Saumur – Town and appellation of Loire Valley, France. Characterful minerally red wines from Cabernet Franc grapes, and some whites.

Sauvignon Blanc – French white grape variety now grown worldwide. The wines are characterised by aromas of gooseberry, fresh-cut grass, even asparagus. Flavours are often described as grassy or nettly.

sec – Dry wine style. French.

secco – Dry wine style. Italian.

Semillon – White grape variety originally of Bordeaux, where it is blended with Sauvignon Blanc to make fresh dry whites and, when harvested very late in the season, the ambrosial sweet whites of Barsac, Sauternes and other appellations. Even in the driest wines, the grape can be recognised from its honeyed, sweet-pineapple, even banana-like aromas. Now widely planted in Australia and Latin America, and frequently blended with Chardonnay to make interesting dry whites.

sherry – The great aperitif wine of Spain, centred on the Andalusian city of Jerez (from which the name sherry is an English corruption). There is a lot of sherry-style wine in the world, but only the authentic wine from Jerez and the neighbouring producing towns of Puerta de Santa Maria and Sanlucar de Barrameida may label their wines as such. The Spanish drink real sherry – very dry and fresh, pale in colour and served well-chilled – called fino and manzanilla, and darker but naturally dry variations called amontillado, palo cortado and oloroso. The stuff sold under the big brand names for the British market are sweetened, coloured commercial yuck for putting in trifles or sideboard decanters to gather dust. The sherries recommended in this book are all real wines, made the way the Spanish like them.

Shiraz – Australian name for the Syrah grape. Ozzie Shirazzes, unlike their silky-spicy southern-French counterparts, tend to be big, muscular and alcoholic wines with earthy darkness.

Somontano – Wine region of northeast Spain. Name means 'under the mountains' – in this case the Pyrenees – and the region has had DO status only since 1984. Much innovative winemaking here, with 'New World' styles emerging. Some very good buys. A region to watch.

souple – French wine-tasting term translates into English as 'supple' or even 'docile' as in 'pliable' but I understand it in the vinous context to mean muscular but soft – a wine with tannin as well as soft fruit.

Spätlese – See QmP.

spirity – Some wines, mostly from the New World, are made from grapes so ripe at harvest that their high alcohol content can be detected through a mildly burning sensation on the tongue, similar to the effect of sipping a spirit.

spritzy – Describes a wine with a barely detectable sparkle. Some young wines are intended to have this elusive fizziness; in others it is a fault.

spumante – Sparkling wine of Italy. Asti Spumante is the best known. The term describes wines that are fully sparkling. *Frizzante* wines have a less-vigorous mousse.

stalky – A useful tasting term to describe red wines with flavours that make you think the stalks from the grape bunches must have been fermented along with the must (juice). Young Bordeaux reds very often have this mild astringency. In moderation it's fine, but if it dominates it probably signifies the wine is at best immature and at worst badly made.

Stellenbosch – Town and region at the heart of South Africa's burgeoning wine industry. It's an hour's drive from Capetown and the source of much of the country's cheaper wine. Quality is variable, and the name Stellenbosch on a label can't (yet, anyway) be taken as a guarantee of quality.

stony – Wine-tasting term for keenly dry white wines. It's meant to indicate a wine of purity and real quality, with just the right match of fruit and acidity.

structured – Good wines are not one-dimensional, they have layers of flavour and texture. A structured wine has phases of enjoyment: the 'attack' or first impression in the mouth; the middle palate as the wine is held in the mouth; the lingering aftertaste.

summer fruit – Wine-tasting term intended convey a smell or taste of soft fruits such as strawberries and raspberries – without having to commit too specifically to which.

Superiore – On labels of Italian wines, this is more than an idle boast. Under DOC rules, wines must qualify for the Superiore designation by reaching one or more specified quality levels, usually a higher alcohol content or an additional period of maturation. Frascati, for example, qualifies for DOC status at 11.5% alcohol, but to be classified Superiore must have 12% alcohol.

Syrah – The noble grape of the Rhône Valley, France. Makes very dark, dense wine characterised by peppery, tarry aromas. Now planted all over southern France and farther afield. In Australia, where it makes wines ranging from disagreeably jam-like plonks to wonderfully rich and silky keeping wines, it is known as the Shiraz.

Tafelwein – Table wine, German. The humblest quality designation – doesn't usually bode very well.

tank method – Bulk-production process for sparkling wines. Base wine undergoes secondary fermentation in a large, sealed vat rather than in individual closed bottles. Also known as the Charmat after the name of the inventor of the process.

tannin – Well-known as the film-forming, teeth-coating component in tea, tannin is a natural compound occurring in black grape skins and acts as a natural preservative in wine. Its noticeable presence in wine is regarded as a good thing. It gives young everyday reds their dryness, firmness of flavour and backbone. And it helps high-quality reds to retain their lively fruitiness for many years. A grand Bordeaux red when first made, for example, will have purply-sweet, rich fruit and mouth-puckering tannin, but after ten years or so this will have evolved into a delectably fruity mature wine in which the formerly parching effects of the tannin have receded almost completely, leaving the shade of 'residual tannin' that marks out a great wine approaching maturity.

tar – On the whole, winemakers don't like critics to say their wines evoke the redolence of road repairs, but I can't helping using this term to describe the agreeably 'burnt' flavour that is often found at the centre of the fruit in wines from Argentina and Italy in particular.

tears – The colourless alcohol in the wine left clinging to the inside of the glass after the contents have been swirled. Persistent tears (also known as 'legs') indicate a wine of good concentration.

Tempranillo – The great black grape of Spain. Along with Garnacha (Grenache in France) it makes all red Rioja and Navarra wines and, under many pseudonyms, is an important or exclusive contributor to the wines of many other regions of Spain. It is also widely cultivated in South America.

tinto – On Spanish labels indicates a deeply coloured red wine. *Clarete* means a paler colour. Also Portuguese.

Toro – Quality wine region east of Zamora, Spain.

Torrontes – White grape variety of Argentina. Makes soft, dry wines often with delicious grapy-spicy aroma, similar in style to the classic dry Muscat wines of Alsace, but at more accessible prices.

Touraine – Region encompassing a swathe of the Loire Valley, France. Non-AC wines may be labelled Sauvignon de Touraine etc.

Trebbiano – The workhorse white grape of Italy. A productive variety that is easy to cultivate, it seems to be included in just about every ordinary white wine of the entire nation – including Frascati, Orvieto and Soave. It is the same grape as France's Ugni Blanc.

Trincadeira Preta – Portuguese black grape variety native to the port-producing vineyards of the Douro Valley (where it goes under the name Tinta Amarella). In southern Portugal, it produces dark and sturdy table wines.

trocken – 'Dry' German wine. It's a recent trend among commercial-scale producers in the Rhine and Mosel to label their wines with this description in the hope of reassuring consumers that the contents do not resemble the dreaded sugar-water Liebfraumilch-type plonks of the bad old days. But the description does have a particular meaning under German wine law, namely that there is only a low level of unfermented sugar lingering in the wine (9 grams per litre, if you need to know), and this can leave the wine tasting rather austere.

Ugni Blanc – The most widely cultivated white grape variety of France and the mainstay of many a cheap dry (not to say acidic) white wine. To date it has been better known as the provider of base wine for distilling into Armagnac and Cognac, but lately the name has been appearing on wine labels. Technology seems to be improving the performance of the grape. The curious name is pronounced 'Oonyee', and is the same variety as Italy's ubiquitous Trebbiano.

Vacqueyras – Village of the southern Rhône valley of France in the region better known for its generic appellation, the Côtes du Rhône. Vacqueyras can date its winemaking history all the way back to 1414, but has only been producing under its own village AC since 1991. The wines, from Grenache and Syrah grapes, can be wonderfully silky and intense, spicy and long-lived.

Valdepeñas – An island of quality-production amidst the ocean of mediocrity that is Spain's La Mancha region – where most of the grapes are grown for distilling into the head-banging brandies of Jerez. Valdepeñas reds are made from a grape they call the Cencibel – which turns out to be a very close relation of the Tempranillo grape that is the mainstay of the fine but expensive red wines of Rioja. Again, like Rioja, Valdepeñas wines are matured in oak casks to give them a vanilla-rich smoothness. Among bargain reds, Valdepeñas is a name to look out for.

Valpolicella – Red wine of Verona, Italy. Good examples have ripe, cherry fruit and a pleasingly dry finish. Unfortunately, there are many bad examples of Valpolicella. Shop with circumspection. Valpolicella Classico wines, from the best vineyards clustered around the town, are more reliable. Those additionally labelled superiore have higher alcohol and some bottle-age.

vanilla – Ageing wines in oak barrels (or, less picturesquely, adding oak chips to wine in huge concrete vats) imparts a range of characteristics including a smell of vanilla from ethyl vanilline naturally given off by oak.

varietal – A varietal wine is one named after the grape variety (one or more) from which it is made. Nearly all everyday wines worldwide are now labelled in this way. It is salutary to contemplate that just 20 years ago, wines described thus were virtually unknown outside Germany and one or two quirky regions of France and Italy.

vegetal – A tasting note definitely open to interpretation. It suggests a smell or flavour reminiscent less of fruit (apple, pineapple, strawberry and the like) than of something leafy or even root-based. Some wines are evocative (to some tastes) of beetroot, cabbage or even unlikelier vegetable flavours – and these characteristics may add materially to the attraction of the wine.

vegetarian wine – Given that proper wine consists of nothing other than grape juice and the occasional innocent natural additive, it might seem facile to qualify it as a vegetable product. But most wines are 'fined' – clarified – with animal products. These include egg whites, isinglass from fish bladders and casein from milk. Gelatin, a beef by-product briefly banned by the UK government at the hysterical height of the BSE scare, is also used. Consumers who prefer to avoid contact, however remote, with these products, should look out for wines labelled suitable for vegetarians and/or vegans. The wines will have been fined with bentonite, an absorbent clay first found at Benton in the US state of Montana.

Verdelho – Portuguese grape variety once mainly used for a medium-dry style of Madeira, also called Verdelho, but now rare. The vine is now prospering in Australia, where it can make well-balanced dry whites with fleeting richness and lemon-lime acidity.

Verdicchio – White grape variety of Italy best known in the DOC zone of Castelli di Jesi in the Adriatic wine region of the Marches. Simple dry white wines once better known for appearing in naff amphora-style bottles.

Vermentino – White grape variety principally of Italy, especially Sardinia. Makes florally-scented soft dry whites.

vin de liqueur – Sweet style of white wine mostly from the Pyrenean region of southwesternmost France, made by adding a little spirit to the new wine before it has fermented out, halting the fermentation and retaining sugar.

Vin Délimité de Qualité Supérieur – Usually abbreviated to VDQS, is a French wine-quality designation between Appellation Contrôlée and vin de pays. To qualify, the wine has to be from approved grape varieties grown in a defined zone. This designation is gradually disappearing.

vin de pays – 'Country wine' of France. The French map is divided up into more than 100 vin de pays regions. Wine in bottles labelled as such must be from grapes grown in the nominated zone or *département*. Some vin de pays areas are huge: the Vin de Pays d'Oc (named after the Languedoc region) covers much of the Midi and Provence. Plenty of wines bearing this humble designation are of astoundingly high quality and certainly compete with 'New World' counterparts for interest and value.

Vin de Pays de l'Hérault – Zone within Languedoc-Roussillon region of southwest France.

Vin de Pays des Coteaux du Luberon – Zone of Provence, France.

Vin de Pays des Côtes de Gascogne – Zone of 'Gascony' region in southwest France.

Vin de Pays de Vaucluse – Zone of southern Rhône Valley, France.

Vin de Pays d'Oc – Largest of the zones, encompasses much of the huge region of the Languedoc of southwest France. Many excellent wines are sold under this classification, particularly those made in appellation areas from grapes not permitted locally.

Vin de Pays du Jardin de la France – Zone of the Loire Valley, France.

vin de table – The humblest official classification of French wine. Neither the region, grape varieties nor vintage need be stated on the label. The wine might not even be French. Don't expect too much from this kind of 'table wine'.

vin doux – Sweet, mildly fortified wine mostly of France, usually labelled *vin doux naturel*. A little spirit is added during the winemaking process, halting the fermentation by killing the yeast before it has consumed all the sugars – thus the pronounced sweetness of the wine.

Vinho de mesa – 'Table wine' of Portugal.

Vino da tavola – The humblest official classification of Italian wine. Much ordinary plonk bears this designation, but the bizarre quirks of Italy's wine laws dictate that some of that country's finest wines are also classed as mere *vino da tavola* (table wine). If an expensive Italian wine is labelled as such, it doesn't mean it will be a disappointment.

vintage – The grape harvest. The year displayed on bottle labels is the year of the harvest. Wines bearing no date have been blended from the harvests of two or more years.

Vino de mesa – 'Table wine' of Spain. Usually very ordinary.

Viognier – A grape variety once exclusive to the northern Rhône Valley in France where it makes a very chi-chi wine, Condrieu, usually costing up to £20. Now, the Viognier is grown more widely, in North and South America as well as elsewhere in France, and occasionally produces soft, marrowy whites that echo the grand style of Condrieu itself.

Viura – White grape variety of Rioja, Spain. Also widely grown elsewhere in Spain under the name Macabeo. Wines have a blossomy aroma and are dry, but sometimes soft at the expense of acidity.

Vouvray – AC of the Loire Valley, France, known for still and sparkling dry white wines and sweet, still whites from late-harvested grapes. The wines, all from Chenin Blanc grapes, have a unique capacity for unctuous softness combined with lively freshness – an effect best portrayed in the demi-sec (slightly sweet) wines, which can be delicious and keenly priced. Unfashionable, but worth looking out for.

weight – In an ideal world the weight of a wine is determined by the ripeness of the grapes from which it has been made. In some cases the weight is determined merely by the quantity of sugar added during the production process. A good, genuine wine described as having weight is one in which there is plenty of alcohol and 'extract' – colour and flavour from the grapes. Wine enthusiasts judge weight by swirling the wine in the glass and then examining the 'legs' or 'tears' left clinging to the inside of the glass after the contents have subsided. Alcohol gives these runlets a dense, glycerine-like condition, and if they cling for a long time, the wine is deemed to have weight – a very good thing in all honestly made wines.

Winzergenossenschaft – One of the many very lengthy and peculiar words regularly found on labels of German wines. This means a winemaking co-operative. Many excellent German wines are made by these associations of growers.

woodsap – A subjective tasting note. Some wines have a fleeting bitterness which is not a fault, but an interesting balancing factor amidst very ripe flavours. The effect somehow evokes woodsap.

Xarel-lo – One of the main grape varieties for cava, the sparkling wine of Spain.

Xinomavro – Black grape variety of Greece. It retains its acidity even in the very hot conditions that prevail in many Greek vineyards – where harvests tend to overripen and make cooked-tasting wines. Modern winemaking techniques are capable of making well-balanced wines from Xinomavro.

yellow – White wines are not white at all, but various shades of yellow – or, more poetically, gold. Some white wines with opulent richness even have a flavour I cannot resist calling yellow – reminiscent of butter.

Zefir – Hungarian white grape variety that can (on a good day) produce spicy dry wine rather like the Gewürztraminer of Alsace.

Zenit – Hungarian white grape variety. Dry wines.

Zinfandel – Black grape variety of California. Makes brambly reds, some of which can age very gracefully, and 'blush' whites – actually pink, because a little of the skin colour is allowed to leach into the must. The vine is also planted in Australia and South America. The Primitivo of southern Italy is said to be a related variety, but makes a very different kind of wine.

Wine rituals

There has always been a lot of nonsense talked about the correct ways to serve wine. Red wine, we are told, should be opened and allowed to 'breathe' before pouring. White wine should be chilled. Wine doesn't go with soup, tomatoes or chocolate. You know the sort of thing.

It would all be simply laughable except that these daft conventions do make so many potential wine lovers nervous about the simple ritual of opening a bottle and sharing it around. Here is a short and opinionated guide to the received wisdom.

Breathing

Simply uncorking a wine for an hour or two before you serve it will make absolutely no difference to the way it tastes. However, if you wish to warm up an icy bottle of red by placing it near (never on) a radiator or fire, do remove the cork first. As the wine warms, even very slightly, it gives off gas which will spoil the flavour if it cannot escape.

Chambré-ing

One of the more pretentious terms in the wine vocabulary. The idea is that red wine should be at the same temperature as the room *(chambre)* you're going to drink it in. In fairness, it makes sense – although the term harks back to the days when the only people who drank wine were those who could afford to keep it in the freezing-cold vaulted cellars beneath their houses. The ridiculously high temperatures to which some homes are raised by central heating systems today are really far too warm for wine. But presumably those who live in such circumstances do so out of choice, and will prefer their wine to be similarly overheated.

Chilling

Drink your white wine as cold as you like. It's certainly true that good whites are at their best at a cool rather than at an icy temperature, but cheap and characterless wines can be improved immeasurably if they are cold enough – the anaesthetising effect of the temperature removes all sense of taste. Pay no attention to notions that red wine should not be served cool. There are plenty of lightweight reds that will respond very well to an hour in the fridge.

Corked wine

Wine trade surveys reveal that far too many bottles are in no fit state to be sold. The villain is very often cited as the cork. Cut from the bark of cork-oak trees cultivated for the purpose in Portugal and Spain, these natural stoppers have done sterling service for 200 years, but now face a crisis of confidence among wine producers. A diseased or damaged cork can make the wine taste stale because air has penetrated, or musty-mushroomy due to a chemical reaction. These faults in wine, known as corked or corky, should be immediately obvious, even in the humblest bottle, so you should return the bottle to the supplier and demand a refund. A warning here. Bad corks tend to come in batches. It might be wise not to accept another bottle of the same wine, but to choose something else.

Today, more and more wine producers are opting to close their bottles with polymer bungs. Some are designed to resemble the 'real thing' while others come in a rather disorienting range of colours – including black. There seems to be no evidence that these synthetic products do any harm to the wine, but it might not be sensible to 'lay down' bottles closed with polymer. The effects of years of contact with these materials are yet to be scientifically assessed.

Corkscrews

The best kind of corkscrew is the 'waiter's friend' type. It looks like a pen-knife, unfolding a 'worm' (the helix or screw) and a lever device which, after the worm has been driven into the cork (try to centre it) rests on the lip of the bottle and enables you to withdraw the cork with minimal effort. These devices are cheaper and longer-lasting than any of the more-elaborate types, and are equally effective at withdrawing the new polymer bungs.

Decanting

Some wines need decanting because they are unfiltered and leave a gritty deposit in the bottom of the bottle. Cheaper wines suffer less from this admirable quirk, but there are plenty of rugged, budget bottles that will benefit from being sploshed into a new container – which could just as easily be another, clean wine bottle (use a funnel) as an elegant decanter. 'Airing' red wines in this way has real benefits, as distinct from the pointless 'breathing' exercise described above.

Glasses

Tricky one, this. Does it make any difference whether you drink your wine from a hand-blown crystal glass or Old Mother Riley's hobnail boot? Do experiment! Conventional wisdom suggests that the ideal glass is clear, uncut, long-stemmed and with a tulip-shaped bowl large enough to hold a generous quantity when filled only halfway up. The idea is that you can hold the glass by its stalk rather than by its bowl. This gives an uninterrupted view of the colour, and prevents you smearing the bowl with your sticky fingers. By filling the glass only halfway up, you give the wine a chance to 'bloom', showing off its wonderful perfume. You can then intrude your nose into the air space within the glass, without getting it wet, to savour the bouquet. It's all harmless fun, really – and quite difficult to perform if the glass is an undersized Paris goblet filled, like a pub measure, to the brim.

Washing up

If your wine glasses are of any value to you, don't put them in the dishwasher. Over time, they'll craze from the heat of the water. And they will not emerge in the glitteringly pristine condition suggested by the pictures on some detergent packets. For genuinely perfect glasses that will stay that way, wash them in hot soapy water, rinse with clean, hot water and dry immediately with a glass cloth kept exclusively for this purpose. Sounds like fanaticism, but if you take your wine seriously, you'll see there is sense in it.

Keeping it

How long can you keep an opened bottle of wine before it goes downhill? Not long. A re-corked bottle with just a glassful out of it should stay fresh until the day after, but if there is a lot of air inside the bottle, the wine will oxidise, turning progressively stale and sour. Wine 'saving' devices that allow you to withdraw the air from the bottle via a punctured, self-sealing rubber stopper are variably effective, but don't expect these to keep a wine fresh for more than a couple of re-openings. A crafty method of keeping a half-finished bottle is to decant it, via a funnel, into a clean half bottle and recork.

Storing it

Supermarket labels always seem to advise that 'this wine should be consumed within one year of purchase'. I think this is a wheeze to persuade customers to drink it up quickly and come back for more. Many of the more robust red wines are likely to stay in good condition for much more than one year, and plenty will actually improve with age. On the other hand, it is a sensible axiom that inexpensive dry white wines are better the younger they are. If you do intend to store wines for longer than a few weeks, do pay heed to the conventional wisdom that bottles are best stored in low, stable temperatures, preferably in the dark. Bottles closed with conventional corks should be laid on their side lest the corks dry out for lack of contact with the wine.

Earthy, ripe, strawberry-nosed Burgundy from Thresher at £8.99.

Wine and food

Wine is made to be drunk with food, but some wines go better with particular dishes than others. It is no coincidence that Italian wines, characterised by soft, cherry fruit and a clean, mouthdrying finish, go so well with the sticky delights of pasta.

But it's personal taste rather than national associations that should determine the choice of wine with food. And if you prefer a black-hearted Argentinian Malbec to a brambly Italian Barbera with your bolognese, that's fine.

The conventions that have grown up around wine and food pairings do make some sense, just the same. I was thrilled to learn in the early days of my drinking career that sweet 'dessert' wines can go well with strong blue cheese. As I don't much like puddings, but love sweet wines, I was eager to test this match – and I'm here to tell you that it works very well indeed as the end-piece to a grand meal in which there is cheese as well as pud on offer.

Red wine and cheese are supposed to be a natural match, but I'm not so sure. Reds can taste awfully tinny with soft cheeses such as Brie and Camembert, and even worse with goat's cheese. A really extravagant, yellow Australian Chardonnay will make a better match. Hard cheeses such as cheddar and the wonderful Old Amsterdam (top-of-the-market Gouda) are better with reds.

And then there's the delicate issue of fish. Red wine is supposed to be a no-no. This might well be true of grilled and wholly unadorned white fish such as sole or a delicate dish of prawns, scallops or crab. But what about oven-roasted monkfish or a substantial winter-season fish pie? An edgy red will do very well indeed, and provide much comfort for those many among us who simply prefer to drink red wine with food, and white wine on its own.

It is very often the method by which dishes are prepared, rather than their core ingredients, that determines which wine will work best. To be didactic, I would always choose Beaujolais or summer-fruit-style reds such as those from Pinot Noir grapes to go with a simple roast chicken. But if the bird is cooked as *coq au vin* with a hefty, winey sauce, I would plump for a much more assertive red.

Some sauces, it is alleged, will overwhelm all wines. Salsa and curry come to mind. I have carried out a number of experiments into this great issue of our time, in my capacity as consultant to a company which specialises in supplying wines to Asian restaurants. One discovery I have made is that forcefully fruity dry white wines with keen acidity can go very well indeed even with fairly incendiary dishes. Sauvignon Blanc with Madras? Give it a try!

I'm also convinced, however, that some red wines will stand up very well to a bit of heat. The marvellously robust Argentinian reds that get such frequent mentions in this book are good partners to Mexican chilli-hot recipes and salsa dishes. The dry, tannic edge to these wines provides a good counterpoint to the inflammatory spices in the food.

Some foods are supposedly impossible to match with wine. Eggs and chocolate are among the prime offenders. And yet, legendary cook Elizabeth David's best-selling autobiography was entitled *An Omelette and a Glass of Wine*, and the affiliation between chocolates and champagne is an unbreakable one. Taste is, after all, that most personally governed of all senses. If your choice is a boiled egg washed down with a glass of claret, who is to say otherwise?

Index